Graphing Calculator **Lab Manual**

TI-81™ TI-82™

Contemporary Precalculus
through applications

Graphing Calculator

LAB MANUAL

TI-81™ TI-82™

John Goebel

Donita Robinson

Nicole Arendas

Janson Publications, Inc.
Dedham, Massachusetts

Revised Edition

Printed in the United States of America.

9 8 7 6 5 1 2 3 4 5 6 7 8 9

CONTENTS

PREFACE

When the Mathematics Department at the North Carolina School of Science and Mathematics first set out to write a new precalculus course, we found very little existing computer software that would graph functions, fit curves to data points, and work with matrices. In spite of this, we set out to write a course that was applications-oriented, that allowed students to investigate patterns and problems, and that took advantage of the capabilities of the computer. In order to implement the course fully, we wrote our own software so that students could easily use the computer as a tool.

By the time our precalculus course, *Contemporary Precalculus through Applications*, was published, we saw several developments which validated the assumptions made while designing the course. First and foremost was the release of the *NCTM Curriculum Standards for School Mathematics.* In that document NCTM recommends that students solve real-world problems and that they use the computer as a tool, to help both in understanding important concepts and in solving problems. NCTM further recommends that students learn to use functions for developing mathematical models.

Another development that has dramatically changed the mathematics classroom, and, as a result, our course, is the continuing evolution of the graphing calculator as a viable instructional tool. Studies indicate that very few mathematics classrooms have a computer together with an adequate projection device for classroom demonstrations. Currently, for the combined cost of one computer and a projection device, a school can put a calculator into the hands of every student in several classrooms. These calculators are powerful teaching tools. By using them, students can do calculations quickly. This helps students notice patterns. They can graph and visualize the behavior of functions; they can plot data and then find a function to model the data; and they can use matrices to solve real and interesting problems. With these tools in the hands of students, we are approaching the goal of making mathematics more accessible to a broader student population. It is our belief that every student, from the strongest to the weakest, will benefit by having a graphing calculator available during class discussions, when doing homework, and when taking tests.

The purpose of this *Graphing Calculator Lab Manual* is to help students and teachers alike more quickly discover and use the power of the graphing calculator. The goal is not to help students do the old mathematics faster or more accurately, but rather to explore some new and exciting mathematics and to think about and mathematically model the world around them. The numerical and graphical capabilities of these calculators will force us all to re-examine continually what we teach and how we teach it. The opportunity for students to learn how to use mathematics and for teachers to teach problem solving may finally be here.

We would like to thank the many teachers who have used the programs and problems in this book and especially the students and our colleagues in the Mathematics Department at the North Carolina School of Science and Mathematics for their helpful suggestions. We would also like to thank Texas Instruments, Inc. for their assistance, and particularly Ann Phipps, who arranged to have this manuscript reviewed for accuracy.

INTRODUCTION

This manual assumes that the user has some experience with the TI-82 or TI-81 Graphic Calculator. At a minimum, the user should go through the Getting Started section and Chapter 1 of the *Guidebook* that comes with the calculator. If further orientation to the calculator is needed, the user should work through the next two chapters of the *Guidebook* and get better acquainted with the features of the calculator, including the modes and menus.

The Modes. Before using your calculator to do anything, it must be set to the proper mode. This is fairly easy to do by pressing the [MODE] key and using the arrows to select the desired mode and pressing [ENTER]. The normal mode settings for most of the explorations and programs in this book are as follows:

Display:	Norm
Decimal Places:	Float
Angle Measure:	Rad
Graphing:	Function
Points:	Connected
Function Plotting:	Sequence
Coordinate System:	Rect

At the beginning of each section and each program, we will tell you if the mode should be anything other than those listed above.

We will use the following convention when instructing you to enter a sequence of keystrokes. We will try to give the exact keystrokes for the processes outlined in the text. These keystrokes will be enclosed in boxes. The symbol in the box will be for the primary function of that key. The symbol following the key strokes (in parentheses) will tell you the actual command the key sequence activates. For example, the sequence of keystrokes [2nd] [MATRX](STAT) means that you will press the [2nd] key followed by the [MATRX] key, but the calculator will respond by displaying the **STAT** menu.

When writing programs to do many of the tasks that the calculator would not do on its own, we aimed to make the programs fairly straightforward. We realize that the user may want to modify a program to make it more versatile or to provide more prompts. We trid to make the programs simple enough so that most users would take the time to ente them and understand how they work. We hope that these rather basic programs will provide an outline that users can follow, modify and improve upon for broader application.

SECTION 1

Linear Data

Scatter Plots

Problem Statement

Archeologists can determine the height of ancient humans by simply finding one bone of the body and using the linear relationship that exists between the length of that bone and height. To find such a relationship, data is gathered from modern man. Using the data in the table below, graph a scatter plot and find a linear relationship between the length of the tibia and height.

tibia in cm	29	31	32	34	35	36	37	39	40	41
height in cm	153	157	159	164	167	169	172	176	179	183

GRAPHING CALCULATOR SOLUTION. To determine if the relationship is linear, we would like to draw a scatter plot on the calculator.

TI-82 instructions. To enter the data into the TI-82 graphing calculator, follow the procedure below:

- Get the Statistics Menu, press [STAT].
- Notice the 2 submenus: **EDIT CALC.**
- Begin by clearing at least two lists of data already in memory. Select **4:ClrList** from the **EDIT** submenu either by pressing the down arrow or by pressing the [4] key. Since there are six lists of numbers, you must also select the list(s) to clear. To do this, press the [2nd] key followed by the number of the list. If more than one list is to be cleared, separate the lists by commas. Be sure to press [ENTER] after selecting the list number. For entering ordered pairs, you will need to clear two lists.

- To enter data, press the [STAT] key again and select **EDIT**. Notice the spreadsheet style format. By pressing the right and left arrows, you can access all six lists.
  - Enter all the first coordinates in List 1. Press [ENTER] after each coordinate.
  - After entering all of the first coordinates, press the right arrow so the cursor jumps to the top of the next empty list.
  - Enter the second coordinate of each ordered pair, pressing [ENTER] after each coordinate.
  - You can enter up to 150 data points, depending on the available memory.
  - Upon entering the last pair of data, press [2nd] and [MODE] (QUIT).
  - If you make a mistake entering a data point, use the up and down arrows to go to the location of the incorrect data and simply type the correct value over the incorrect value.
- To see the scatter plot of this data, press the [2nd] and [Y=] key (STAT PLOT) and set one of the Plots to contain the lists which contain your data. To do this
  - Select the Plot number, press [ENTER] and use the arrows to select **On**. Press [ENTER].
  - Move down and select the Scatter plot graph type.
  - Move down and select the list which contains the first-coordinates.
  - Move down again and select the list which contains the second-coordinates.
  - Move down and select the type of marker to indicted the points on the graph.
  - After making all of the above choices, press [ZOOM] and select **9:ZOOMSTAT**, either by using the down arrow and [ENTER] keys or by pressing the [9] key. Notice that the TI-82 automatically sets the domain and range for the data.

TI-81 instructions. To enter the data into the TI-81 graphing calculator, follow the procedure below:

- Get the Statistics Menu, press [2nd] [MATRX].
- Notice the 3 submenus: **CALC DRAW DATA**.
- Begin by clearing data already in memory. Select the **DATA** submenu and select **2:ClrStat** to clear the statistics memory. Be sure to press [ENTER] twice, once to select the option and once to execute it.

- Also clear functions for graphing, or at least make sure that none of the functions are highlighted. To pull up functions press [Y=]. To clear the functions, place the cursor to the right of each equal sign and press [CLEAR]. To leave a function in memory, but not have it highlighted, place the cursor over the equal sign and press [ENTER].

- To enter data, pull up **STAT** menu again (Press [2nd] [MATRX]).

  - Select the **DATA** submenu.
  - Select **1:Edit**.
  - Press [ENTER].
  - You will see: x1=
y1= 1
  - Type in each coordinate followed by [ENTER].
    * You can enter up to 150 data points, depending on the available memory.
    * When entering univariate data, the y1= prompt can be used for frequencies.
  - Upon entering the last pair of data, press [2nd] and [CLEAR].
  - If you make a mistake entering a data point, use the up and down arrows to go to the location of the incorrect data and simply type the correct value over the incorrect value.

- **Before graphing anything, be sure to set the range. Let** $25 \le x \le 45$ **and** $150 \le y \le 200$.

Once the data points are entered, the next step is to plot them in a scatter plot. To do this:

- Select the **STAT** menu once more ([2nd] [MATRX]).
- Select **DRAW**.
- Select **2:Scatter** and press [ENTER] twice.

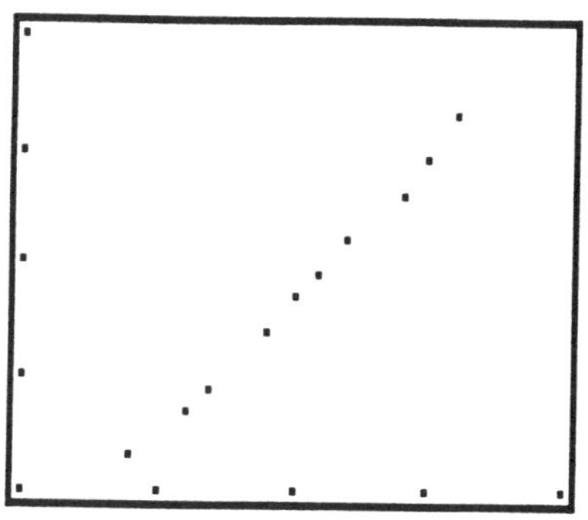

Many keystrokes are required in the process above just to graph a scatter plot. The program below will accomplish the same results with fewer strokes to remember and key in. See Section 8 for instructions for entering a program.

Note. The last section of this book gives some programming hints, but throughout the book it is assumed that the user is familiar with the keys and menus of the TI-81. You may need to refer to your *TI-81 Graphics Calculator Guidebook*.

PROGRAMMING SOLUTION. To cut down on the number of key strokes, you may want to write a short program to enter data and plot the scatter plot.

Program Code: SCATTER

Program Code	**Comments**
:ClrDraw	From the Draw Menu
:All-Off	From the **Y-VARS** Menu
:ClrStat	From the Stat Menu
:Disp "NO. POINTS"	
:Input N	Set number of data points
:0 →J	Initialize counter (Press 0 [STO] J)
:Lbl 1	Begin data input loop
:J+1 →J	
:Disp "X="	
:Input A	Input x-coordinate
:A → {x}(J)	Store x-coordinate in list
:Disp "Y="	
:Input B	Input y-coordinate
:B → {y}(J)	Store y-coordinate in list
:If J<N	Check for end of list
:Goto 1	End of input loop
:Scatter	Draw scatter plot
:End	

Before running the scatter program, be sure to set the range to accommodate the data and make sure that no functions are highlighted in the [Y=] edit screen.

Additional Problems

1. The times (in seconds) for the 100 meters backstroke for women at the Olympics are given in the following table. Does the relationship seem to be linear? If a line were used to model this data, how would the slope of the line be interpreted?

Date	Time	Date	Time	Date	Time
1924	83.20	1952	74.30	1972	65.80
1928	82.00	1956	72.90	1976	61.83
1932	79.40	1960	69.30	1980	60.86
1936	78.90	1964	67.70	1984	62.55
1948	74.40	1968	66.20	1988	60.89

2. The life expectancy of males born between 1920 and 1988 are given in the following table. What type of relationship exists between the life expectancy and the year of birth?

Date	1920	1930	1940	1950
Years	53.6	58.1	60.8	65.6
Date	1960	1970	1980	1988
Years	66.6	67.1	70.0	71.5

Source: U.S. Dept. of Health and Human Services, National Center for Health Statistics

3. The size of families in the United States has been decreasing in recent years. The following table gives the average size of U. S. households from 1940 to 1990. Make a scatter plot and describe the relationship.

Date	1940	1950	1955	1960	1965
Size	3.67	3.37	3.33	3.33	3.29
Date	1970	1975	1980	1985	1990
Size	3.14	2.94	2.76	2.69	2.63

Source: U.S. Bureau of the Census

Linear Data and the Median-Median Line

Models for Linear Data

If the ordered pairs of data appear linear, you can fit a line to the data. Two common lines used to model linear data are the median-median line and the least squares regression line. Both give a relationship between the length of the tibia and height for the archeology problem on page 1. The median-median line can be computed by hand fairly easily and has the advantage that it is resistant to data points that appear to be out of line with the rest of the data set. The TI-82 will find the median-median line automatically. The regression line, or least squares line, while more widely used, is more difficult to find. Both the TI-82 and TI-81 will find the slope and intercept of this line for you. (See Section 5: "Linear Data and the Least Squares Line".)

Problem Statement

A basketball is dropped from different heights and the height of the bounce is measured. Find the relationship between the height of the drop and the height of the bounce.

MEDIAN-MEDIAN LINE SOLUTION. The scatter plot for this data reveals that there appears to be a linear relationship. One of the linear equations that can be used to model this relationship is the median-median line. To find the equation of this line, divide the data set into three fairly equal groups. Since the medians of subgroups of the data are to be used, the data should be put in increasing order. To do this, order the first coordinates. Be sure to keep the ordered pairs together as they are divided into three groups. Once the first coordinates of each group are in order, find the median for these coordinates. Next find the median for the second coordinates of the first subgroup of data. The point described by the ordered pair formed from the medians of the first and second coordinates is the lower summary point. The height and bounce data below serves as an example:

height (in)	41	43	45	47	49	51	53	55	57	59
bounce (in)	27	28	29	30	32	33	34	35	36	37

The median height for the lower group is 43 and the median bounce is 28. For the second group, the median height is 50 and the median bounce is 32.5. For the upper group, the median height is 57 while the median bounce is 36. These are the summary points. The slope of the median-median line will be the slope of the line connecting the lower and upper summary points. In this example, the slope is

$$(36 - 28)/(57 - 43) = 57142857\ldots.$$

The line joining these points will probably not pass through the middle summary point, but this summary point will influence the line. The line must be shifted one-third of the way to the middle summary point, while keeping the slope equal to the slope of the line through the two outer summary points. This could all be done by hand, and part of this process is actually easier to do by hand. Finding the summary points of the three subgroups is easy to do by hand. Programming the TI-81 to find the summary points is possible, but probably not worth the effort. Given the summary points, the following program will compute the slope, find the vertical distance between the middle summary point and the line, and shift the line one-third of the way toward the summary point. The program will then display the slope and the y-intercept of the line and plot the line over the scatter plot of the set of data.

TI-82 instructions. The TI-82 has the median-median line built into the Statistics Menu. To graph the median-median line along with the scatter plot of a set of data, simply do the following:

- Press the [STAT] key and select **CALC.**
- Select **4:Med-Med** by pressing the down arrow or the [4] key. Be sure to press [ENTER] when the **Med-Med** prompt appears on the screen.
- Notice that you are given the form of the equation, the slope, and the intercept.
- Press [Y=] and move the cursor to an empty function. Be sure all other functions are not selected.
- Now press the [VARS] key and select **5:Statistics** from this menu.
- Use the right arrow to select the **EQ** option and select **7:RegEQ**. As soon as you select this option, the equation for the median-median line will be filled in.
- All that remains now is to press the [GRAPH] key. The domain and range were preset by the **ZoomStat** option when you graphed the Scatter Plot.

PROGRAMMING SOLUTION. After finding the three summary points, run the following program to find the median-median line and graph it with the scatter plot of the data set.

Before running the median line program, be sure to set the range to accommodate your data. The program will define the function Y_3 to be $Y_3 = MX + B$. Initially this will be the line through the two outer summary points, but in the end it will be the median-median line.

Program Code: MEDIAN LINE

Program Code	**Comments**
:ClrDraw	From Draw Menu.
:All-Off	From **Y-VARS** Menu.
:Disp "INPUT LOWER SUMMARY POINT"	
:Input A	Enter median of x-coordinates of lower subset
:Input B	Enter median of y-coordinates of lower subset
:Disp "INPUT MIDDLE SUMMARY POINT"	
:Input C	Enter median of x-coordinates of middle subset
:Input D	Enter median of y-coordinates of middle subset
:Disp "INPUT UPPER SUMMARY POINT"	
:Input E	Enter median of x-coordinates of upper subset
:Input F	Enter median of y-coordinates of upper subset
:(F−B)/(E−A)→M	Compute slope
:-AM+B →B	Determine y-intercept of first line
:C →X	Store x-coordinate of middle summary point in X
:"MX + B" →Y_3	Store equation of line
:Y_3 →W	Compute y-coordinate on the line for C
:(D−W)/3+B →B	Slide line one-third of the way toward to the middle summary point
:Disp "SLOPE"	
:Disp M	Display the slope
:Disp "INTERCEPT"	
:Disp B	Display the y-intercept
:Pause	Pause to display slope and intercept
:Scatter	Draw the scatter plot
:DispGraph	Graph median-median line
:End	

Linear Models and a Residual Program

The best way to determine how well a linear model—either the median-median line or a regression line—fits a set of data is to look at the residuals.

GRAPHING CALCULATION SOLUTION. It is very easy to look at the residuals for any model using the TI-82. This can be done directly from the keyboard, or you may want to write a simple program to make the process even more automatic. For the program and the TI-81 solution, see the programming solution that follows.

If you wish to examine the residuals for a linear model (or any model), and you don't want to do any programming, follow these steps:

- First be sure that the data set is entered so that the independent variable is stored in list $\mathbf{L}_1$ and the dependent variable in list $\mathbf{L}_2$ and a linear model stored as function Y_1.
- Next press [STAT] and select **4:ClrList**. At the **ClrList** prompt, press [2nd] and [3] ($\mathbf{L}_3$) followed by [ENTER].
- Now press [STAT] again and select **EDIT** and move the cursor so that it covers the $\mathbf{L}_3$ label. Here we want to substitute the values in list $\mathbf{L}_1$ into function $\mathbf{Y}_1$ and subtract these from the values in list $\mathbf{L}_2$. To do this simply press [2nd] [2] ($\mathbf{L}_2$) [−] [2nd] [VARS] (Y-VARS) and select **1:Function**. Now select **1:**$\mathbf{Y}_1$, followed by [(] [2nd] [1] ($\mathbf{L}_1$) and [)]. The bottom line of the calculator should be

$$L_3 = L_2 - Y_1(L_1)$$

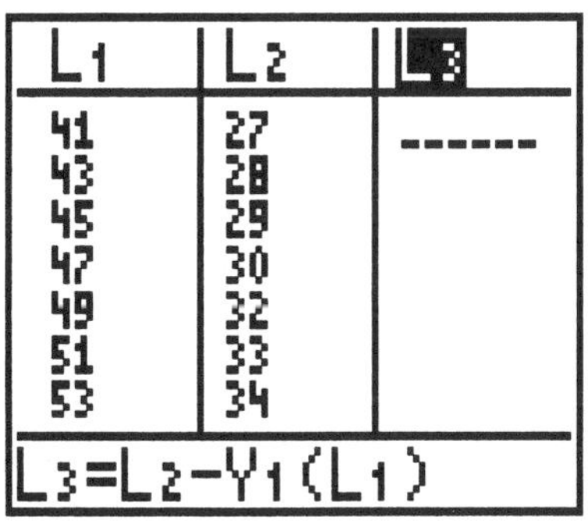

As soon as you press [ENTER], this list will contain the residuals.

- Now you want to plot list $\mathbf{L}_1$ versus list $\mathbf{L}_3$ so you must change the **STAT PLOT** options. Press [2nd] [Y=] and turn off the first plot (containing the ordered pairs of the original data). To do this, select **1:Plot1...**, move the cursor to **Off**, and press [ENTER]. Press [2nd] [Y=] again and select **2:Plot2....** Turn this plot on, select the scatter plot graph type, be sure that the **Xlist** contains $\mathbf{L}_1$ and that the **Ylist** contains $\mathbf{L}_3$. You can select any mark for the residuals.

- Press ZOOM and select **9:ZoomStat**.

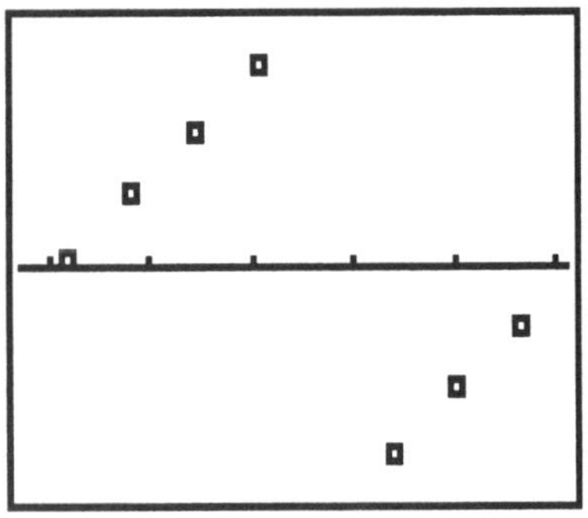

PROGRAMMING SOLUTION.

TI-82 instructions. If you are going to investigate residuals several times, it may well be worth your while writing a program to cut down on the number of keystrokes. You will still need to enter the data into lists $\mathbf{L}_1$ and $\mathbf{L}_2$ and the equation of the function modeling the data into function $\mathbf{Y}_1$. Once this is done, the following program does the rest. To enter the program, press PRGM and select **NEW** followed by the name of the program.

Program Code: RESIDUAL

Program Code	Comments
:FnOff	Turns all functions off.
:PlotsOff	Turns all plots off.
:Plot1(Scatter,L1,L2,□)	This section plots the
:ZoomStat	scatter plot of the original data.
:Pause	
:DrawF Y_1	Graphs the model stored as Y_1.
:Pause	
:PlotsOff 1	
Plots2(Scatter,L1,L3,□)	This section plots the residuals.
:ZoomStat	
:Pause	
:Disp "MIN RESIDUAL"	This section displays the
:Disp min(L_3)	minimum and maximum values
:Disp "MAX RESIDUAL"	of the residuals.
:Disp max(L_3)	

When you run the program, you will first see the scatter plot of the orginal data. Press ENTER and the median-median line will be drawn along with the data points. Press ENTER again and you will see the residual plot. Pressing ENTER one more time displays the minimum and maximum values of the residuals. You may wish to leave off the last section of the program and use the TRACE key to see the actual values of the residuals on the graph. You can also go to the **STAT** menu and see the list of residuals in the spreadsheet format.

TI-81 instructions. To use the TI-81 to look at the residuals, implement the program on the following page, provided a linear model is stored as function Y_3.

With a data set entered and a linear model stored as function Y_3, you can now run this program. It will automatically find the residuals, graph them, and show the value of the largest and smallest residual. Upon running the program, you will first see the graph of the residuals. Press [ENTER] to see the values of the smallest and largest residual. Press [GRAPH] key to return to the residual plot and the [CLEAR] key to toggle back to the residual range.

If the data is linear, or nearly linear, the residuals should be randomly scattered about the linear model. If this is not the case, you probably should not try to model the data with a linear function.

The graph on the left shows the residuals for the tibia and height data set using the median-median line. The screen on the right shows the minimum and maximum residuals. Since there is no pattern to the residuals, and they are relatively small in comparison to the original data, the linear model used is an acceptable one to use for the given data set.

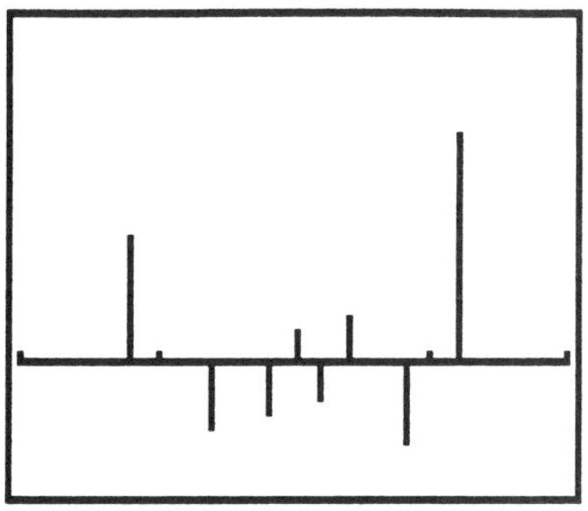

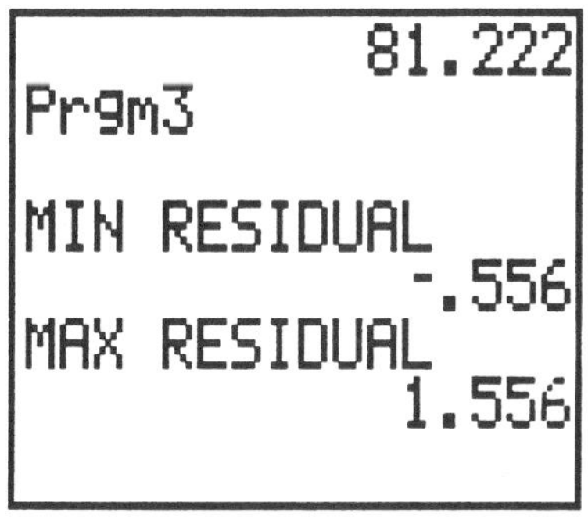

Program Code: RESIDUAL

Program Code	Comments
:All-Off	
:ClrDraw	
:0 →J	This section sets the
:0 →Ymin	range for the residual
:0 →Ymax	plot.
:Lbl 3	
:J+1 →J	
:{x}(J) →X	Setting Ymax to 1.5 times
:{y}(J)−Y_3 →R	the greatest positive residual.
:If R >Ymax	
:R →Ymax	
:If R<Ymin	Setting Ymin to 1.5 times
:R →Ymin	the smallest negative residual.
:If J<Dim{x}	
:Goto 3	
:1.5Ymax →Ymax	
:1.5Ymin →Ymin	
:0 →J	
:Line(Xmin,0,Xmax,0)	Drawing the x-axis.
:Lbl 2	
:J+1 →J	
:{x}(J) →X	
:{y}(J)−Y_3 →R	Computing and
:Line(X,0,X,R)	plotting the residuals.
:If J<Dim{x}	
:Goto 2	
:Pause	
:2*Ymin/3 →Q	The greatest positive residual.
:2*Ymax/3 →W	The smallest negative residual.
:Disp ""	
:Disp "MIN RESIDUAL"	
:Disp Q	
:Disp "MAX RESIDUAL"	
:Disp W	
:End	

SECTION 2

Functions

Toolkit of Elementary Functions

Problem Statement

Determine the characteristics of the elementary functions. Notice the local behavior (near the origin), the global behavior (the big picture), and the overall behavior of each function.

Enter each of the following functions and graph each using the **ZStandard** (TI-82) or **Standard** (TI-81) window for the non-trigonometric functions and the **ZTrig** (Ti-82) or **Trig** (TI-81) window for the trigonometric functions. You can access both of these windows by pressing the [ZOOM] key and selecting the correct option.

Elementary Functions. The toolkit of elementary functions includes: $y = c$, $y = x$, $y = |x|$, $y = x^2$, $y = x^3$, $y = \frac{1}{x}$, $y = \sqrt{x}$, $y = e^x$, $y = \ln x$, and $y = \sin x$.

- To enter the functions, press [Y=] and enter the rule on any one of the available lines. If the = sign is highlighted, the function will be graphed. Turn the highlighting off by moving the cursor over the equal sign and pressing [ENTER].
- Enter one function at a time and graph the function using the **ZStandard** or **Standard** viewing window. Use the **ZTrig** or **Trig** window for the sine function.
- TI-82: Press the [ZOOM] key and select **MEMORY**. From this menu select **4:SetFactors...**. Set the zoom factors to 2. Press the [ZOOM] key again and select **2:Zoom In**. At this time a blinking cursor appears and can be moved to any point in the viewing window. This point will be the center of the new viewing window. Press [ENTER] again to zoom. Repeat this process to zoom in close to the origin.

- TI-81: Press the ZOOM key and set the zoom factors to 2. Press the ZOOM key again and select **2:Zoom In.** At this time a blinking cursor appears and can be moved to any point in the viewing window. This point will be the center of the new viewing window. Press ENTER again to zoom. Repeat the process to zoom in close to the origin.

- Now press the ZOOM key again. Press the **Zoom Out** key and zoom out far from the origin to see the global behavior.

Many of the functions used by mathematicians and scientists are simply variations of the function list above. A thorough understanding of these functions is important.

Piecewise Defined Functions. The TI-82 and TI-81 allow you to combine function definitions with logical statements to graph piecewise functions. Suppose you want to graph the function which is defined as follows:

$$f(x) = \begin{cases} 4 & \text{if } x < -1 \\ (x-1)^2 & \text{if } x \geq -1 \end{cases}$$

- Press Y= and enter $(X < -1)4 + (X \geq -1)(X - 1)^2$.

- Set the range to $-5 \leq x \leq 5$ and $-3 \leq y \leq 15$.

- Press GRAPH to see the function.

For any given X value, the calculator will assign a value of 0 to the expression $(X < -1)$ if it is false and a value of 1 if it is true. Similarly for the expression $(X \geq -1)$. Consequently, for any X, the function will be

$$(0)4 + (1)(x - 1)^2$$

or

$$(1)4 + (0)(x - 1)^2.$$

You can see how this feature allows one to use two formulas to define one piecewise function.

Additional Problems

Answer each of the following for the above toolkit functions.

1. Which functions are symmetric with respect to the y-axis? Try graphing $f(x)$ and $f(-x)$. If the two are the same, the graphs are symmetric with respect to the y-axis. These functions are called *even functions.*

2. Which functions are symmetric with respect to the origin? Graph $f(-x)$ and $-f(x)$. If these are indistinguishable, the function is symmetric with respect to the origin. Such functions are called *odd functions.*

3. Note the domain and range of each function. The calculator will graph a function over a large window by simply ignoring any undefined values. Evaluate the functions yourself for positive values, negative values, and zero, to determine the domain and range.

4. Graph the piecewise function

$$f(x) = \begin{cases} 4 & \text{if } x < -2 \\ x^2 & \text{if } x \geq -2 \text{ and } x \leq 2 \\ 4 & \text{if } x > 2 \end{cases}$$

Table of Values of a Function

Problem Statement

If money is invested in the bank at 6.5%, compounded monthly, how long (to the nearest month) will it take for the money to double?

GRAPHING CALCULATOR SOLUTION. One technique for answering any question about a function is to write the function, graph it, and use the [TRACE] key to move the cursor along the curve. Another way to look at a function is to look at a table of values. The formula for compounding interest is

$$f(x) = A_0\left(1 + \frac{r}{n}\right)^x$$

where A_0 is the initial amount invested, r is the annual interest rate, n the number of compounding periods per year, and x the number of months the amount is invested.

TI-82 instructions. The TI-82 has a very nice table feature. You can display X and values for each of the functions you have defined. With this table feature it is very easy to compare the growth at 6.5% to the growth at several other interest rates. In order to see a table of values, follow the following steps:

1. To set up the table, press [2nd] [WINDOW] (TblSet) and enter 0 for the TblMin value. This is the minimum X-value for the table. Also enter a value for the ΔTbl. This is the increment in the X-coordinate. Since, the independent variable here is the number of months, entering a 1 for ΔTbl will show the interest at the end of each month. Entering a 12 will show the interest at the end of each year. You can also select **Auto** or **Ask** for each variable. Auto fills in the table starting at the TblMin and incrementing by ΔTbl, while Ask allows you to input any value for the independent variable and prompt the calculator to compute a value of the dependent variable.

2. Press **Y=** and enter the function in Y_1 using specific values for A_0, r, and n. If you wish, you can enter similar functions for Y_2 to Y_0.

3. Now press [2nd] [GRAPH] (TABLE) and you will see a spreadsheet-like table with 7 rows and two or three columns (depending on how many functions you have selected). You can scroll up, down or to the right to see additional values. If you want to scroll to values below the TblMin, the cursor must be in the X-column.

TI-81 instructions. To view a single value of the function, first store the function in Y_1, using specific values for A_0, r, and n. Now store an x-value in X by pressing [2] [→] [X | T] [ENTER]. To see the value of the function for the x you just stored, you must press [2nd] and [VARS] (Y-VARS) followed by [ENTER] [ENTER].

Programming Solution. The TI-81 procedure is very tedious if you want to see several values, but the following program will greatly shorten the process and display seven values of the function. When you run the program enter a starting x-value and a step size (either positive or negative). The program will compute the y-coordinate for the initial x-value and the next six values, storing them in a 1 by 2 matrix so that the x- and y-coordinates will be displayed on the same line. Since the screen only displays 16 characters per line, you may want to limit the decimal places so that you can see part of both coordinates. (The matrix will take 4 places for its brackets, comma, and a space.)

Program Code: TABLE

Program Code	**Comments**
:Disp "INPUT X"	
:Input X	Enter initial value.
:Disp "INPUT STEP"	
:Input S	Enter step size.
:0 →I	Initialize counter.
:1 →Arow	Set row dimension for Matrix A.
:2 →Acol	Set column dimension for Matrix A.
:Lbl 1	Begin loop to compute 7 values.
:X →[A](1,1)	Store X as 1st coordinate of Matrix.
:Y1 →[A](1,2)	Store Y_1 as 2nd coordinate of Matrix.
:Disp [A]	Display Matrix A.
:S+X →X	Increment X by S.
:I+1 →I	Increment counter.
:If I ≤ 6	Condition to end loop.
:Goto 1	End loop.

Now run the program and at the first prompt, enter the initial value for x. At the second prompt, enter the step size.

Additional Problems

Use graphs or a table of values to find the following:

1. If the account above paid 8% annually instead of 6.5%, how soon would the amount double?

2. When an object with mass 1 unit is shot into the air at angle θ with some air resistance, (proportional to the velocity), the height at any given time can be given by the function

$$h(t) = (9.8 + V_0 \sin\theta)(1 - e^{-t}) - 9.8t.$$

a. To find the range of the projectile, we need to know when it hits the ground. Assume that $V_0 = 100$. Find the value of $t, t > 0$, for which $h(t)$ equals zero. Vary the value of θ from 10 to 20 degress and record your answers. When does the projectile stay up the longest?

b. The horizontal component for the projectile is

$$x(t) = V_0 \cos\theta(1 - e^{-t}).$$

For each value of θ above, find the range for the value of t found above to make the height zero. What angle results in the greatest range?

3. When population growth is unconstrained, the population model is exponential. When the growth is constrained, the function is called logistic. For the logistic function

$$f(t) = \frac{500}{1 + 4e^{-0.1t}}$$

use a table of values to evaluate the function for $-30 < t < 30$.

a. What value does the function approach as t gets large?

b. At what point on the graph does the y-value reach half way to the maximum value?

c. When is the population growing at the fastest rate?

Transformations of Functions

Problem Statement

Determine how the following transformations change the graph of the function $f(x)$.

$$f(x) + c; \quad f(x + c); \quad cf(x); \quad f(cx).$$

GRAPHING CALCULATOR SOLUTION. Enter the simple function $f(x) = x^2$ as Y_1 and $Y_2 = X^2 + 2$.

- To enter the functions, press [Y=].
- To enter $f(x) = x^2$, press [X,T,θ] followed by [x^2]. The function $f(x)$ is now called Y_1.
- Press [ENTER]. Now the cursor is in position for you to enter the second function. Press [X,T,θ] [x^2] [+] [2]. The function $g(x)$ is now stored in Y_2. Notice that the equal sign is highlighted for these two functions. Be sure that the other functions are either cleared (move the cursor to the right of each equal sign and press [CLEAR]), or that the equal sign of the other function is not highlighted (move the cursor on top of the equal sign and press [ENTER]). To store these functions and return to the home screen, press [2nd] [MODE] (QUIT) on the TI-82 or [2nd] [CLEAR] on the TI-81.
- Before graphing you must determine the viewing window. Press [WINDOW] (TI-82) or [RANGE] (TI-81).
  - — Now enter the values for Xmin, Xmax, Xscl, Ymin, Ymax, Yscl. Leave the Xres set to 1. For the range variables you may choose the following:

    Xmin = −3
    Xmax = 3
    Xscl = 1 (Note, each tick mark on the x-axis will equal 1 unit.)
    Ymin = −1
    Ymax = 9
    Yscl = 1 (Note, each tick mark on the y-axis will equal 1 unit.)

- Now the calculator is ready to graph the functions. Press [GRAPH].

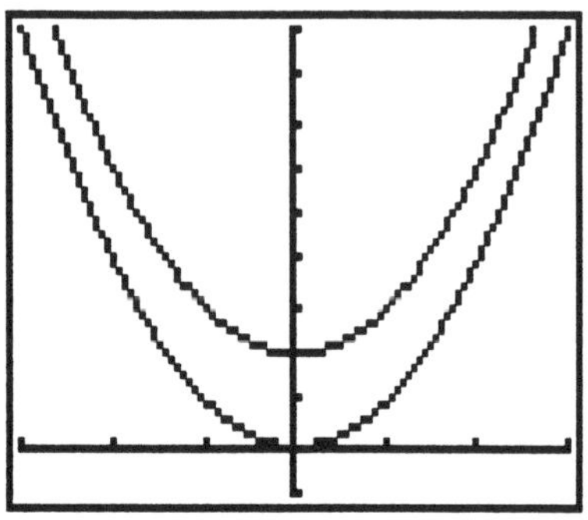

- If the calculator is set in **Sequence** mode (press [MODE] and select the desired modes), it will graph Y_1 first, followed by Y_2. If the calculator is set to **Simul** mode, it will graph the two functions simultaneously. Clearly, the graph of Y_2 is simply Y_1 moved up by 2 units. If Y_2 is changed to $x^2 - 1$, what is likely to happen?

Transformations of Polar Graphs. The TI-82 will plot polar functions as nicely as it does rectangular functions. Polar functions are written as $r(\theta)$ and you may enter as many as six polar functions. Enter a polar function such as $r(\theta) = \sin(\theta)$. Now investigate the transformations $r_2(\theta) = r_1(\theta) + C$, $r_3(\theta) = r_1(\theta + C)$, $r_4(\theta) = C \cdot r_1(\theta)$, and $r_5(\theta) = r_1(C\theta)$.

The steps here are very similar to the steps for entering rectangular functions:

- First press the [MODE] key and select **Pol** for polar graphing.
- Now press [Y=] and enter $\sin(\theta)$ as function r_1.
- Enter $r_1(\theta) + C$ for r_2, $r_1(\theta + C)$ for r_3, $Cr_1(\theta)$ for r_4, and $r_1(C\theta)$ for r_5. When defining one polar function in terms of another, you can find the function names in the [2nd] [VARS] (Y-VARS) menu.
- Before you graph the transformations, you will need to store a value in C, set the viewing window, and graph the original graph by itself. To set the viewing window press [WINDOW] and set the following values:

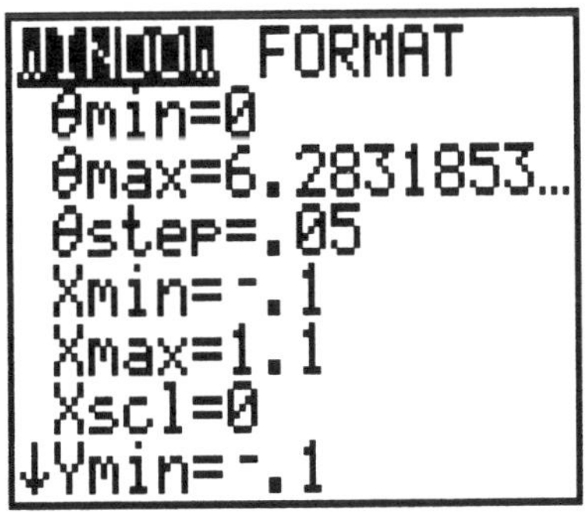

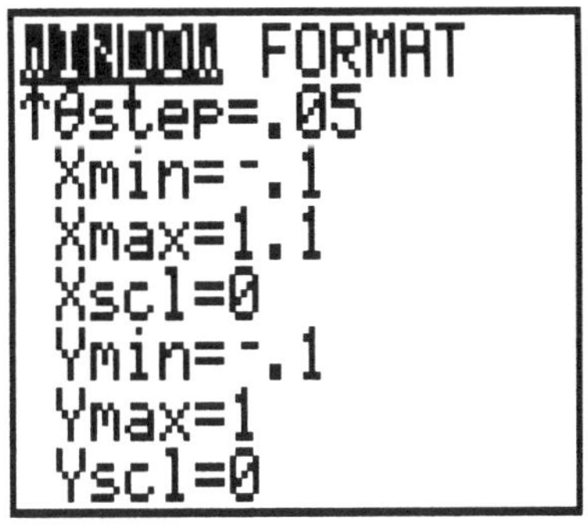

  Note that you can enter 2π for θmax and $\pi/100$ for θstep.

- Turn on the original function and one of the transformations. Be sure you have stored a reasonable value for C.
  - For the transformation $r_1(\theta) + C$, try values for C between -1 and 1.
  - For the transformation $r_1(\theta + C)$, try values for C between $-\frac{\pi}{2}$ and $\frac{\pi}{2}$.
  - For the transformation $Cr_1(\theta)$, try values for C between 0.5 and 1.5.
  - For the transformation $r_1(C\theta)$, try values for C like $\frac{1}{4}$, $\frac{1}{3}$, $\frac{1}{2}$, 2, 3, 4.
- Press [GRAPH] after you have selected one function and entered a value for C.

Additional Problems

Determine how altering the equation of a toolkit function "transforms" the graph of the function.

1. Make a generalization of how the graph of $f(x+c)$ differs from the graph of $f(x)$, where c is a constant.

Graph each pair of functions on the same set of axes.

a. $f(x) = x^3$ $\quad g(x) = (x+2)^3$

b. $f(x) = \dfrac{1}{x}$ $\quad g(x) = \dfrac{1}{x-1}$

c. $f(x) = \sqrt{x}$ $\quad g(x) = \sqrt{x+3}$

2. Make a generalization of how the graph of $f(cx)$ differs from the graph of $f(x)$, where c is a constant.

Graph each trio of functions on the same set of axes.

a. $f(x) = |x|$ $\quad g(x) = |2x|$ $\quad h(x) = |\frac{1}{2}x|$

b. $f(x) = \sin(x)$ $\quad g(x) = \sin(3x)$ $\quad h(x) = \sin(\frac{1}{3}x)$

c. $f(x) = \sqrt{x}$ $\quad g(x) = \sqrt{4x}$ $\quad h(x) = \sqrt{\dfrac{x}{4}}$

d. $f(x) = e^x$ $\quad g(x) = e^{-2x}$ $\quad h(x) = e^{-\frac{1}{2}x}$

3. Make a generalization of how the graph of $cf(x)$ differs from the graph of $f(x)$, where c is a constant.

Graph each trio of functions on the same set of axes.

a. $f(x) = x$ $\quad g(x) = 2x$ $\quad h(x) = 0.5x$

b. $f(x) = x^2$ $\quad g(x) = 4x^2$ $\quad h(x) = \frac{1}{4}x^2$

c. $f(x) = \sin(x)$ $\quad g(x) = 3\sin(x)$ $\quad h(x) = \frac{1}{3}\sin(x)$

4. How does the graph of $g(x) = 3|x-1|+2$ compare to the graph of $f(x) = |x|$?

Composition of Functions

Problem Statement

Explain how the function $f(x) = |x^2 - x - 2|$ can be seen as the composition of two functions. Use decomposition of functions to graph $f(x)$.

GRAPHING CALCULATOR SOLUTION. Let $f(x) = g(x) \circ h(x) = g(h(x))$, where $h(x) = x^2 - x - 2$ and $g(x) = |x|$. Enter into the calculator $h(x)$ as function Y_1 and $|Y_1|$ as Y_2.

- Press the [Y=] key and enter $x^2 - x - 2$ for Y_1 and abs(Y_1) for Y_2.
- Press [ZOOM] key and select **6:ZStandard** (TI-82) or **Standard** (TI-81).

- If the calculator is in **SEQUENCE** mode, it will first graph $h(x)$ and then $g(h(x))$.
- Press the MODE key and select the **Simul** mode. Now press ZOOM and select **6:Standard**. This time the two graphs will be graphed simultaneously. When are the graphs of $h(x)$ and $g(h(x))$ the same? When are they different?

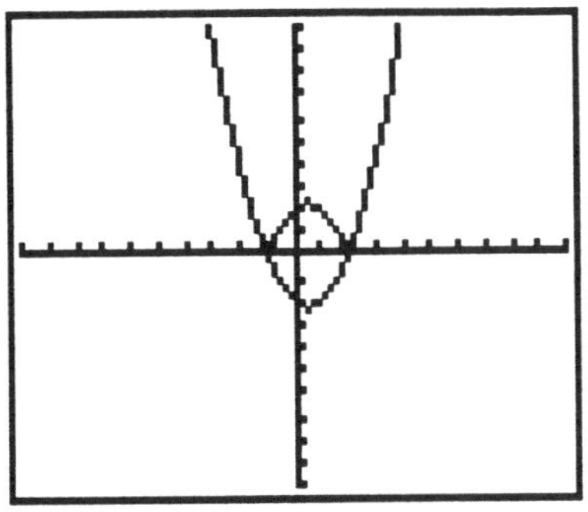

Additional Problems

Explain how the following functions can be written as a composition of functions. Use decomposition to explain the graph of each function. How does the domain of $f(x)$ compare to the domains of the component functions?

1. $f(x) = \dfrac{1}{x^2 - 2}$

2. $f(x) = \sqrt{9 - x^2}$

3. $f(x) = \left|\dfrac{1}{\sin(x)}\right|$.

4. $f(x) = (|x| - 2)^3 - 1$

5. The composition of two linear functions is itself a linear function. Given $f(x) = 2x - 1$ and $g(x) = 3x + 2$, graph $f(g(x))$ and $g(f(x))$. What other conclusion about the composition of functions is suggested by these graphs?

Inverse Functions and Relations

Problem Statement

The population since 1790 in North Carolina can be approximated by the exponential equation $p = 383467e^{0.0148(t-1790)}$. Such an approximation or model roughly fits the data for past years and can be used to predict the approximate population for years in the near future. Suppose you would like to know in what year the population will reach 10 million or any other level.

GRAPHING CALCULATOR SOLUTION. Perhaps the simplest way to answer any question about this function is to trace along the graph until the coordinates of the point are close to either the year or the population level of interest. Another solution involves solving the equation for the year (t), given any desired population level. If it is possible to solve uniquely for the original independent variable, you could form the inverse function and simply substititute in the population and find the year. The inverse function for the population would be

$$t = 1790 + \frac{\ln p - \ln 383467}{0.0148}.$$

To graph this function, the domain and range (of $p(t)$) need to be interchanged.

- Store the inverse function $Y_2 = 1790 + (\ln X - \ln 383467)/0.0148$.
- Store 10,000,000 in X (10000000 [STO] [X,T,θ] [ENTER]). Press [2nd] [VARS] (Y-VARS) and select **1:Function** ··· (TI-82) then **2:Y$_2$**. Press [ENTER] (you must press [ENTER] twice on the TI-81) to see the year in which the model predicts that the population will reach 10,000,000.

Graphs of a Function and its Inverse Function

If a function has an inverse relation that is also a function, both can be stored as functions (as Y-variables). In order to graph the function and its inverse on the same graph, the viewing window must be restricted to the same interval for both the x- and y-coordinates. The graph of both functions reveals several interesting facts about functions and inverses.

- Graph $y = 2x - 3$ and its inverse, $y = \frac{x+3}{2}$, on the window $x \in [-10, 10]$, $y \in [-10, 10]$.
  - Zoom in on the point of intersection. Note the coordinates of this point.
  - Enter the function $y = x$ as Y_3. Press [ZOOM] and select **6:ZStandard** or **Standard** to graph all three functions. What do you notice?
- Graph $y = e^x$ and $y = \ln x$ on the window $x \in [-3, 3]$ and $y \in [-3, 3]$.
- Graph $y = x^3$ and $y = \sqrt[3]{x}$ on the window $x \in [-10, 10]$ and $y \in [-10, 10]$. Zoom in by setting both of the zoom factors to 3. Press [ZOOM], select **MEMORY** (TI-82), then select **4:Set Factors**. Enter 3 for both the XFactor and the YFactor. With the TI-81, press [2nd] [CLEAR] to store these factors. Press [ZOOM] again and select **2:Zoom In**. You will first see the original graph with a blinking cursor. The center of the new window will be the point under this cursor. Leave the cursor at the origin. Press [ENTER] again, and the calculator will zoom in by the a factor of 3 in each direction.

Graphs of a Function and its Inverse Relation

If you cannot uniquely solve for the independent value of a function in terms of the dependent variable, the function is not one-to-one. That is, there is more than one y for some of the x's, and hence there is no inverse function. The TI-82 will draw a function and its inverse relation. Press [Y=] and enter the function. Then press [2nd] [PRGM] (DRAW) and select **8:DrawInv**. Select the function from the Y-VARS menu and press [ENTER]. The following program will plot points on the function and its inverse relation on the TI-81.

Program Code: INVERSE RELATION GRAPHS

Program Code	Comments
:ClrDraw	Clear the graphing window.
:All-Off	
:Xmin →A	
:Xmax →B	
:(B−A)/201 →D	Defining the x-increment.
:A →X	
:Lbl 1	
:Y_1 →Y	
:PT-On(X,Y)	Plotting points of the function.
:PT-On(Y,X)	Plotting points of the inverse.
:X+D →X	Incrementing X.
:If X < Xmax	
:Goto 1	
:End	

- After the program is entered, press the [2nd] key followed by the [CLEAR] key. This stores the program.
- Be sure you have entered into function Y_1 the original function. Try $y = x^2$. Be sure that none of the other functions are highlighted.
- A square viewing window works best here. Press [ZOOM] and select **6:Standard**.
- The program can now be run.
- In order to run a program, press the [PRGM] key and either arrow down to this program or press the program number or letter, followed by [ENTER].

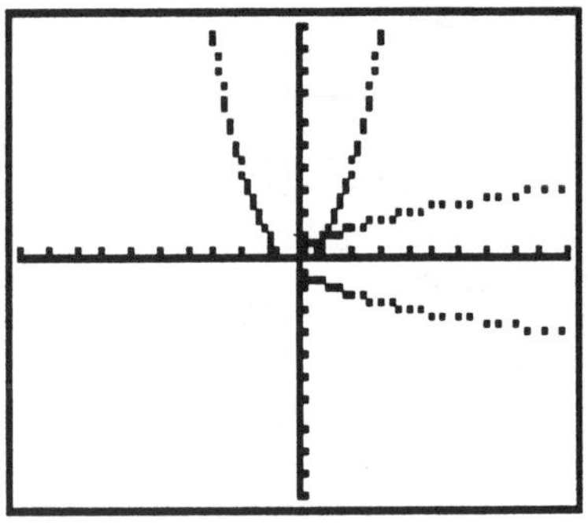

Solving Inequalities

Problem Statement

The average temperature in Durham can be modeled by the trigonometric functions $f(x) = 60 - 21\cos\left(\dfrac{\pi x}{6}\right)$, where x is the month number from 1 through 12. A certain crop will only grow when the average temperature is greater than 45 degrees. Of course, the assumption is that when the temperature averages 45 degrees Fahrenheit, it does not dip below freezing.

GRAPHING CALCULATOR SOLUTION. We want to know when the function $f(x) = 60 - 21\cos(\frac{\pi x}{6})$ is greater than 45. We could graph $f(x)$ and $g(x) = 45$ and find where $f(x) > g(x)$. We can then shade the desired region and by finding the points of intersection, determine the desired interval.

- Press $Y =$ and enter $60 - 21\cos\left(\dfrac{\pi x}{6}\right)$ as Y_1, and 45 as Y_2. Be sure you have selected radians as the unit of angular measurement.
- Set the range so that $0 \le x \le 12$ and $35 \le y \le 85$.
- Press [2nd] [PRGM] (DRAW) and select **7:Shade.** Now press [2nd] [VARS] (Y-VARS) and select **1:Function** ... (TI-82) then $\mathbf{Y}_2$. Enter a comma ([ALPHA] [·] on the TI-81) and again press [2nd] [VARS] (Y-VARS). This time select $\mathbf{Y}_1$ and close the parentheses. The desired region which represents the growing season will be shaded.

- Use the trace feature to find the endpoints of the desired interval.

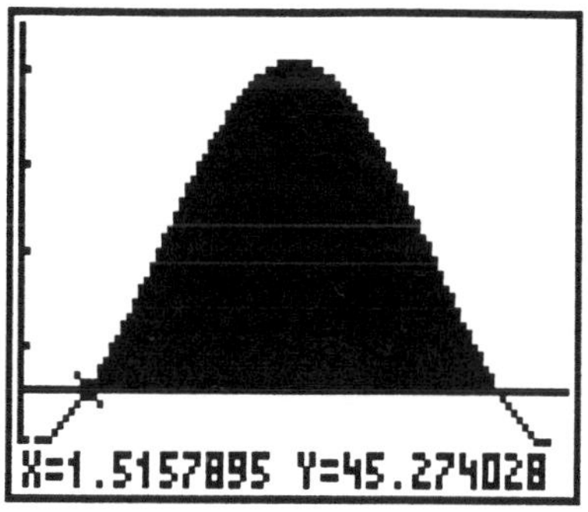

- By pressing the [ZOOM] key and selecting **1:ZBOX** (TI-82) or **BOX** (TI-81) you can zoom in on the point(s) of intersection. When you zoom, the shading will disappear.

Additional Problems

1. The surface area of a cylindrical can which holds 1000 cm^3 can be written as a function of the radius r. The function is $S(r) = 2\pi r^2 + \dfrac{2000}{r}$. For what value of r is the surface area less than 650 cm^2?

2. The formula for finding the payment on an installment loan is given by

$$P(L, r, n) = \frac{rL(1+r)^n}{(1+r)^n - 1},$$

where L is the amount of the loan, r the monthly interest rate, and n the number of monthly payments. If $L = \$10,000$ and $r = 0.0125$, for how many months should you take out a loan so that the payments are less than \$250 per month?

SECTION 3

Polynomial and Rational Functions

Investigating Graphs of Polynomials

Because polynomial functions only involve simple addition and multiplication, including raising real numbers to integral powers, it is relatively easy to work with them. In trying to find a relationship between two quantities, we usually turn first to polynomial functions. When these fail, we may go on to other functions, but even these other functions often end up being approximated or modeled by polynomials. By looking at graphs of polynomial functions, we can observe several properties. These include

- the global behavior of the function and its graph,
- the local behavior, including zeros and turning points, and
- the relationship between zeros and factors.

Problem Statement

Graph each of the following polynomials. Look at the global behavior as well as the local behavior. Using the graph that shows the local behavior, estimate the zeros (to the nearest tenth) and record the number of turning points.

GRAPHING CALCULATOR SOLUTION. Pressing the **ZOOM** key, and selecting the standard window ($-10 \leq x \leq 10$), will yield the global behavior of the following functions. Zoom in enough then to see the zeros and the turning points.

1. $y = x^3 - 3x^2 - 6x + 8$
2. $y = -x^3 + x^2 - 7x - 7$

3. $y = x^4 - 3x^2 - 12x + 5$

4. $y = x^4 - 2x^3 - 19x^2 + 36x - 12$

5. $y = x^5 - 3x^4 - 10x^3 + 18x^2 + 24x$

6. $y = x^4 + 3x^3 + x^2 - 3x - 2$

7. $y = -2x^4 + 8x^3 - 6x - 1$

8. $y = x^3 - x + 1$

9. $y = x^6 - x^2 + 9$

Additional Problems

Based on your observations, write a concise statement of the relationship between the degree of a polynomial and the number of zeros and turning points. Also, write about the role of the leading coefficient and the constant term in the graph of the polynomial.

Turning Point Algorithm: Locating Maximum and Minimum Points

Problem Statement

The post office allows for the girth plus the length of a package to be up to 108 inches. If we assume that a rectangular package has a square base and perpendicular sides, what is the maximum volume the package can have?

GRAPHING CALCULATOR SOLUTION. If we can find a function for the volume of the packages with the given parameters, we can graph it. The TI-82 has a built-in algorithm for finding maximum and minimum values. These values can be estimated on the TI-81 by using the trace and zoom features.

- Let the girth be $4x$ and the length l. Then $4x + l \leq 108$. The volume will be $x^2 l$, or $x^2(108 - 4x)$. Press [Y=] and enter the function in the terms of x.

TI-82 instructions. Now press [2nd] [TRACE] (CALC) and select **4:maximum**. You will be prompted to enter the lower bound of the interval. By using the left and right arrows you may move the blinking cursor to any point on the graph. Select a point to the left of the maximum point and press [ENTER]. You will now be prompted for the upper bound. Select a point to the right of the maximum point and press [ENTER]. Next you will be prompted for a guess. Select a point close to the maximum point. Upon pressing [ENTER], the calculator will execute its algorithm and find the maximum in the given interval.

TI-81 instructions.

- Determine an appropriate domain for x. Obvious choices are $x \geq 0$ and $x \leq 27$. Why? Since we don't know the range, start with $0 \leq y \leq 15000$. Set the domain and range and graph the function. Use the TRACE feature to move near the maximum point of the function.

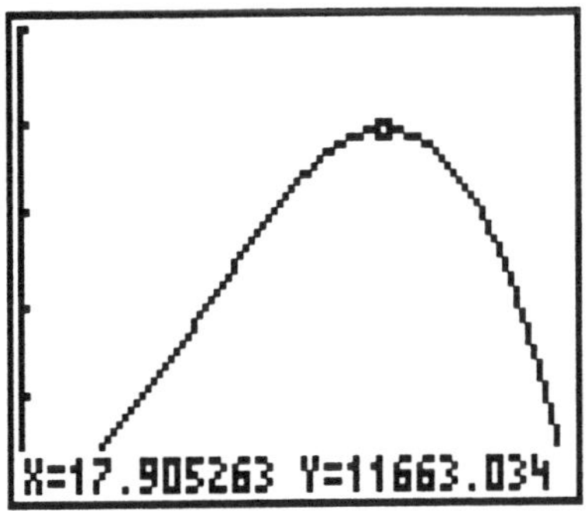

- Press ZOOM and select option **1: Box**. Move the cursor slightly to the left and above the maximum point. Press ENTER. Now move the cursor slightly to the right and below the maximum point. As soon as you press ENTER, the calculator will use the zoom box you have just defined as the new graphing window. Your graph may vary somewhat from this one, depending upon how far you move the cursor in defining the new graphing window.

- You can now retrace and zoom again, each time increasing the resolution of the points and getting a better estimate for the maximum point.

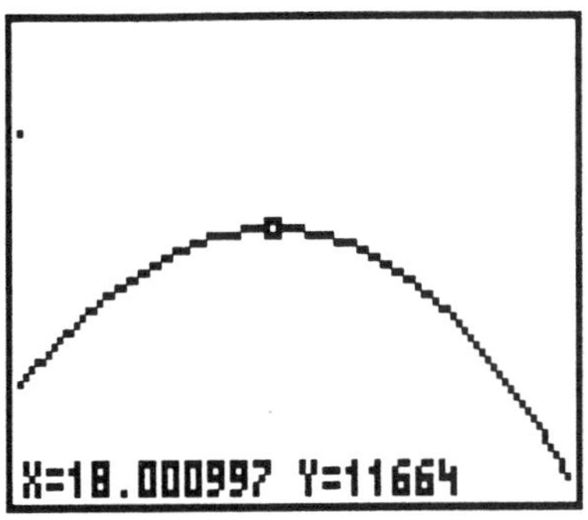

Programming Solution. There is a nice algorithm that will find the maximum point to a prescribed degree of accuracy. You can include it in a program that will automatically find the numerical approximation for the extreme point.

The algorithm requires you again to define the function and graph it to get some idea where the maximum occurs. Using the x-coordinate of a point to the left of the maximum point, the algorithm moves in steps of a prescribed size, finds the y-value for that x, and continues until the y-value begins to decrease. It then backs up a couple of steps and starts the process again, this time using a smaller step size.

The following program initially steps over by tenths, and each time it begins again, the step size is decreased by a factor of 10. Once two successive x-coordinates are within the prescribed degree of accuracy, the program stops.

Note. This program is set up to find a maximum point. By changing the first > to a < sign, you could use the same program to find minimum points.

Program Code: MAXMIN

Program Code	**Comments**
:1 →S	
:Disp "PT. LEFT OF MAX/MIN"	
:Input B	
:Lbl 1	Begin loop to locate turning point.
:.1*S →S	Set initial step size.
:Lbl 2	Begin loop to check for increasing function.
:B →A	Set left endpoint (A) equal to B.
:A + S →B	Set right endpoint (B) equal to $A + S$.
:A →X	Store A as X.
:Y1 →W	Store $f(A)$ as W.
:B →X	Store B as X.
:Y1 →Z	Store $f(b)$ as Z.
:If Z > W	Determine if $f(x)$ is still increasing.
:Goto 2	If so, go back to beginning of loop 2.
:A − S →B	If not, back up a step, store $A - S$ as B.
:If abs (A − B) > .1∧ 5	If A and B too far apart,
:Goto 1	go to beginning of loop 1.
:1 →Arow	Set dimension of Matrix A.
:2 →Acol	
:A →[A](1,1)	Store the x-coordinate in Matrix A.
:W →[A](1,2)	Store the y-coordinate in Matrix A.
:Disp "MAX/MIN AT (X,Y)"	
:Disp [A]	Display Matrix A.
:End	

With the program written and saved, you are now ready to execute it.

- Be sure you have entered function as Y_1.
- In order to run a program, press PRGM. The **EXEC** mode should be highlighted. Press the program number for the MAXMIN program or use the down arrow to highlight the number of this program.

- Press [ENTER] and input a value to the left of the maximum point. The program will display both the x- and y-coordinates of the maximum point when the left and right points are withing 0.1^5. The program will be more accurate if the power is increased to a number greater than 5.

Additional Problems

1. Assume the base of the package (in the above problem) is a circle with diameter x instead of a square. Write the function for the volume and find the maximum volume of this package.
2. Three major cities are located on a grid system with coordinates $(0, -10)$, $(10, 5)$, and $(20, -15)$. The telephone company wants to put a switching station along a road that follows the x-axis of the grid system and lay cable in straight lines from the station to each of the three cities. Where should they place the station to minimize the length of cable required?

Zero-Finding Algorithms

Problem Statement

We want to form an open rectangular box by cutting squares from the corners of an 18 by 24 inch rectangle and folding up the flaps to form a box. The box should hold 624 cubic inches.

TI-82 SOLUTION. The TI-82 has combined an algorithm for locating roots or zeros of a function with the graph of the function. The procedure for finding the zero of the a function is as follows:

- Recall that we are trying to find where $f(x) = x(18 - 2x)(24 - 2x)$ equals 624. So that we can find a root or zero of an equation, enter $x(18-2x)(24-2x) - 624$ and store as function Y_1. Be sure that the other functions are turned off.
- Determine an appropriate domain for x. For example, you might choose $x \geq 0$ and $x \leq 9$ for the domain and for the range $-200 \leq y \leq 200$. Set the viewing window using your domain and range. Now graph the function.
- Now press [2nd] [TRACE] (CALC) and select **2:root**. You will be prompted to enter the lower bound of the interval. By using the left and right arrows you may move the blinking cursor to any point on the graph. Select a point to the left of the zero and press [ENTER]. You will now be prompted for the upper bound. Select a point to the right of the zero and press [ENTER]. Next you will be prompted for a guess. Select a point close to the zero. Upon pressing [ENTER], the calculator will execute its algorithm and find

the zero in the given interval. Notice from the graph that there are two zeros for this function, meaning that there are two different boxes that will have a volumn of 624.

TI-81 SOLUTION. To find when the function $f(x) = x(18-2x)(24-2x)$ equals 624, graph $f(x)$, and $g(x) = 624$. By tracing and zooming, we can approximate the point(s) of intersection.

- Press [Y=] and enter $x(18-2x)(24-2x)$ as Y_1 and 624 as Y_2.
- Set the range so that $0 \le x \le 9$ and $0 \le y \le 1000$.
- Press [Graph] to graph both functions. Use the **TRACE** feature to move the cursor to the point(s) of intersection.
- By pressing the [ZOOM] key and selecting **1: Box**, zoom in on the point(s) of intersection. (Your graph may vary from the one shown here, depending on how your calculator is set and your choice of zoom box.)

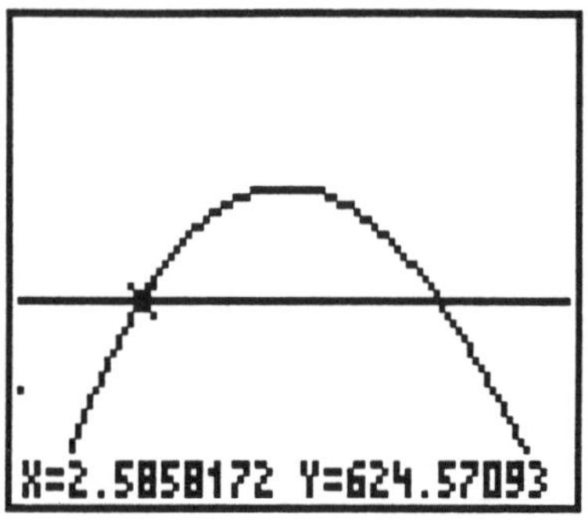

Frequently, the first step in solving an equation is to set one side of the equation equal to zero.

- To do this on the calculator, set Y_3 equal to $Y_1 - Y_2$. First, press [Y=] and then move down to Y_3. Press [2nd] [VARS], (Y-VARS), and with **1: Y_1** highlighted, press [ENTER]. Then press [−] and again press [2nd] [VARS], (Y-VARS), and with **2: Y_2** highlighted, press [ENTER]. To graph only Y_3, move the cursor over the = signs for Y_1 and Y_2 and, if they are highlighted, press [ENTER].
- Set the range so that $0 \le x \le 9$ and $-100 \le y \le 100$. Store these range values and press [GRAPH].
- Again, use the **ZOOM** and **TRACE** features to locate the zero(s) of equation Y_3. (Your result may vary slightly from those shown here, depending on how your calculator is set.)

PROGRAMMING SOLUTIONS. There are two nice algorithms that can easily be programmed into the TI-81 and used to find the zero(s) of equations. Like many numerical algorithms, both have limitations, but used carefully, they can find many approximations for zeros of equations for which analytical solutions are difficult or impossible.

Bisection Algorithm. The Bisection Algorithm begins by taking two x-coordinates, one with a positive y-coordinate and one with a negative y-coordinate. By finding the midpoint between these two x-coordinates, finding the y-coordinate of the midpoint, and replacing the original point whose y-coordinate has the same sign, this algorithm continually bisects the interval on the x-axis until the endpoints of the interval are as close as is desired.

Program Code: BISECT

Program Code	**Comments**
: Disp "LEFT ENDPOINT ="	Enter a point to the
: Input A	left of the zero.
: Disp "RIGHT ENDPOINT = "	Enter a point to the
: Input B	right of the zero.
: Lbl 1	Begin loop.
: A → X	Assign A to X to find
: Y_3 → M	$f(A)$.
: (A+B)/2 → X	Find the midpoint.
: Disp X	Display intermediate solutions.
: Y_3 → C	Finding y-coordinate of midpoint.
: If CM ≥ 0	Replace A with X if the signs of
: X → A	their y-coordinates are the same.
: If CM ≤ 0	Replace B with X if the signs of
: X → B	their y-coordinates are different.
: If abs(A−B) ≥ .1∧10	If A and B are too far apart,
: Goto 1	go back to beginning of the loop.
: Disp "ZERO AT X ="	Display the zero.
: Disp X	
: End	

Before attempting to run this program, make sure that the function for which you are trying to find a zero is stored as Y_3. To execute the program, press [PRGM], select the EXEC mode, select the number of the program, and press [ENTER]. You will need to input two values, one with a negative y-coordinate and one with a positive y-coordinate.

In general, what limitations may arise when using the Bisection Algorithm?

Secant Algorithm. A second algorithm works even when a zero is located at a point of tangency of the function and the x-axis, and it is usually faster than the Bisection Algorithm. This algorithm draws the secant line between two points on the function and then finds the zero of this line. By discarding one of the original points and replacing it with the point whose x-coordinate is the zero of the previous secant line, this algorithm will quickly zoom in on a zero of the function.

Program Code: SECANT

Program Code	Comments
: Disp "FIRST VALUE ="	Input any x-value.
: Input A	
: Disp "SECOND VALUE = "	Input any other x-value.
: Input B	
: Lbl 1	Begin loop.
: A → X	Find $f(A)$.
: Y3 → W	
: B → X	Find $f(B)$.
: Y3 → Z	
: (Z−W)/(B−A) → M	Find slope of segment AB.
: A → B	
: -W/M+A → A	Let A equal the zero of the line AB.
: If abs(W) ≥ .1∧8	If A and B are too far apart,
: Goto 1	go to top of the loop.
: Disp "ZERO AT X ="	Display the value of the zero.
: Disp A	
: End	

Before attempting to run this program, make sure that the function for which you are trying to find zero(s) is stored as Y_3. When you run the program you will need to input two values, but unlike the Bisection Algorithm, you do not need to make sure that the y−coordinates have different signs.

In general, what limitations may arise when using the Secant Algorithm?

Additional Problems

1. The cost of postage stamps has gone up exponentially in recent years. The cost function may be given by $c(t) = 0.04e^{0.065t}$, where t represents years

after 1958. According to this function, when will the cost pass the \$0.50 level? the \$1.00 level?

2. The sales revenue from the sale of ski equipment is cyclic, roughly following the function $f(x) = 150 + 450\cos(\frac{\pi x}{6})$, where x is months after January 1 and $f(x)$ is the revenue per day in dollars. Over what part of the year does the store sell more than \$500 of ski equipment per day?

Picard's Method: Locating Points of Intersection

Problem Statement

Find the point of intersection of the line $y = x$ and the parabola $f(x) = Rx(1-x)$. Try values of R ranging from 0.5 to 4.0. This is an easy problem to solve algebraically, but it does illustrate Picard's method nicely. Picard's method, as an example of iteration, behaves unexpectedly. This section is more of an investigation of this behavior than a means of finding points of intersection.

GRAPHING CALCULATOR SOLUTION. Obviously we could graph the two functions and zoom in on the point of intersection. We will first use the recursive feature of the calculator to solve the problem.

- Store the value 1.5 as R.
- Enter an initial value for x, say 0.05. Press ENTER.
- Now enter $R \cdot$ ANS $\cdot (1 -$ ANS$)$. Press ENTER.
- Each additional time you press ENTER the previous answer is substituted back into the function. Press ENTER until the successive values displayed don't change.

PROGRAMMING SOLUTION. The following program can be used to perform the above steps and at the same time generate a graphical display of the solution.

- The program generates the web diagram associated with the function. Pick some initial x-value and the program will draw the vertical line to the point $(x, f(x))$, followed by the horizontal line to the point $(f(x), f(x))$. The program then goes into a loop, letting $f(x)$ from the last point plotted serve as the new x-coordinate. The process is repeated until either the point of intersection is found or a preset number of iterations is performed without finding the point.

- First let $Y_1 = X$ and $Y_2 = RX(1 - X)$.
- Set the viewing window to be $-0.1 \le x \le 1.1$ and $-0.1 \le y \le 1$. The program will set the upper limit for y for the different values of R.
- Enter the program in Edit mode and then run the program. At the prompt, enter an initial value for x. An initial guess of around 0.1 usually works well.
- On the TI-82, replace the first two lines with

  :{1,2} → dim[A]

  using the MATRIX key and the **MATH** submenu.

Program Code: PICARD

Program Code	**Comments**
:1 →Arow	From **VARS - DIM** menu.
:2 →Acol	
:ClrDraw	
:Disp "INPUT R-VALUE"	
:Input R	
:R/3.5 →Ymax	Setting Maximum value of Y.
:Disp "INPUT INITIAL X"	
:Input A	
:DispGraph	
:A →X	
:Y_2 →B	Finding $f(x)$.
:Line(A,0,A,B)	First vertical line.
:Lbl 1	Begin loop.
:Line(A,B,B,B)	Drawing horizontal lines.
:B →A	$f(x)$ becomes new x.
:A →X	Store A as X.
:Y_2 →B	Store $f(A)$ as B.
:Line(A,A,A,B)	Drawing vertical lines.
:If abs(A−B) ≤ .1 ∧ 11	Is A close enough to B?
:Goto 2	If so, jump out of loop.
:Goto 1	If not, go back through main loop.
:Lbl 2	
:A →[A](1,1)	Store x-coordinate in Matrix A.
:B →[A](1,2)	Store y-coordinate in Matrix A.
:Pause	
:Disp [A]	
:End	

With the program written and saved, you are ready to execute it.

- Be sure you have entered the function as $Y_1 = X$, and $Y_2 = RX(1 - X)$.
- Enter a value for R. Use values for R between 0 and 4.
- Now run the program. Press PRGM. The **EXEC** mode should be highlighted. Press the program number for the PICARD program or use the down arrow to highlight the number of this program.
- Press ENTER and input an initial value for x. If the point of intersection is an attraction point, the web will spiral into the point. With repelling points, the web will move out from the point of intersection. If Picard's algorithm fails to converge, press ON to stop the program.
- When (or if) the programs stops running, press ENTER to see the point of intersection. You will discover that some web diagrams don't appear to converge or diverge but seem to bounce around forever. You might want to add steps to the program to limit the number of times it goes through the loop before stopping. If the program does not stop on its own, press the **ON** key. Select **2:Quit**.

The figures below show the graphical output from the above program. The graph on the left shows the web diagram for $R = 2.5$ while the one on the right is for $R = 3.5$. The values generated in the first graph approach the point (0.6, 0.6) while the values on the right seem to bounce around and never approach one number. Experiment with the value of R and determine the values for which the algorithm **a.** converges to one value, **b.** bounces between 2 values, and **c.** bounces between 4 values. You may have slightly different graphs if you began with a different range.

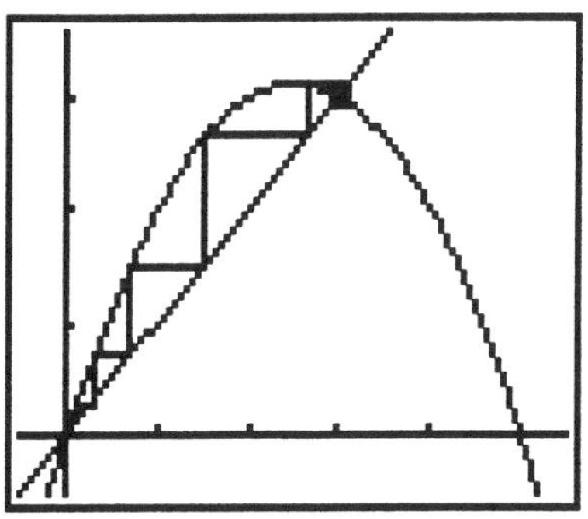

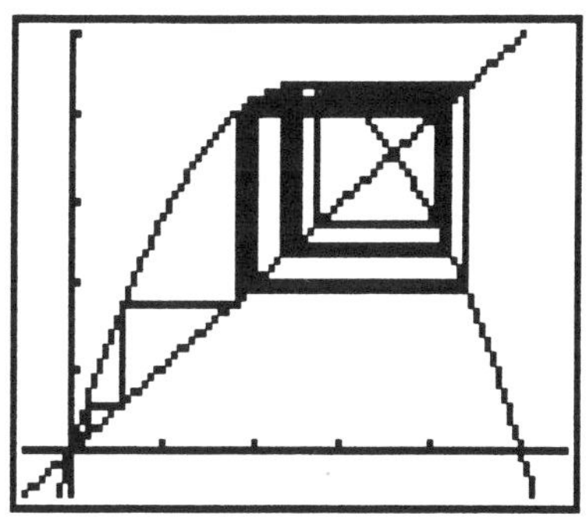

Additional Problems

1. Find the point of intersection of $y = x$ and $y = \cos x$.
2. Solve $3x = e^x$ using Picard's method. **Hint.** By graphing, you will see that there are 2 solutions. First, use $y = x$ and $y = \frac{1}{3}e^x$. Then use $y = x$ and $y = \ln 3x$.
3. Solve $x^2 = \cos x$ using Picard's method.

Graphs of Rational Functions

Problem Statement

Graph the rational function

$$f(x) = \frac{x^2 - x - 6}{x - 1}.$$

Examine the global and local behavior.

GRAPHING CALCULATOR SOLUTION. An examination of the equation of $f(x)$ shows that the function is undefined at $x = 1$. Long division shows that

$$f(x) = x + \frac{-6}{x - 1}.$$

- Set the domain to be $[-5, 5]$ and the range $[-20, 20]$.
- Enter the function in either form and store it as Y_1.
- Press the GRAPH key.
- The graph of $f(x)$ approaches the vertical asymptote $x = 1$ as the x-values approach 1. Tracing along the curve illustrates that as x approaches 1 from the right, y approaches negative infinity and as x approaches 1 from the left, y approaches positive infinity. Here is the graph.

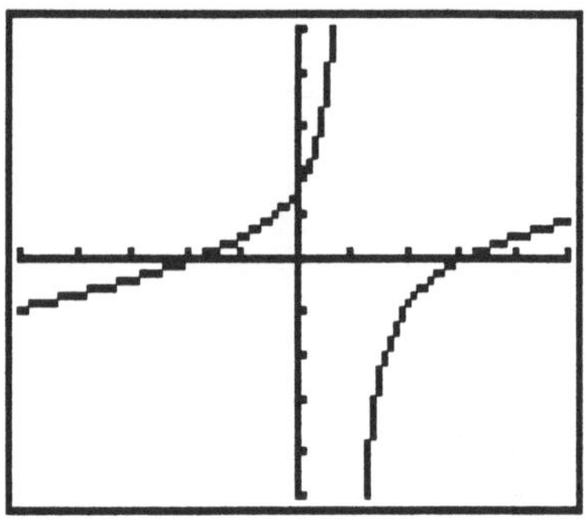

Now let's explore what $f(x)$ looks like as x gets very large or very small; in other words, let's look at the global picture.

- Set the domain to be $[-50, 50]$ and the range $[-50, 50]$.

- Press the GRAPH key.

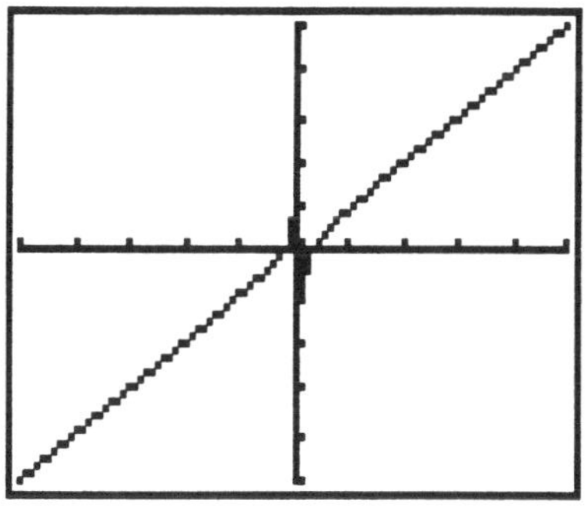

- Now the graph of $f(x)$ looks very much like the graph of the line $y = x$. Tracing along the function shows that it is very close to being $y = x$. Why does this graph look linear and the first graph not?

Asymptotes. Normally a rational function can have two of three types of asymptotes. Horizontal and oblique asymptotes are relatively easy to see when looking at a global picture of the graph. The vertical asymptote is more difficult to see. In the above example, the line $y = x$ is an oblique asymptote and $x = 1$ is a vertical asymptote.

Additional Problems

Find appropriate windows to view both the local and global behavior of the following rational functions. Note the asymptotes of each function.

1. $f(x) = \dfrac{3x}{x-2}$.

2. $g(x) = \dfrac{x^2 - 5x + 1}{x - 2}$.

3. $h(x) = \dfrac{x^2 - x - 6}{x - 3}$.

4. $k(x) = \dfrac{x^3 - x^2 - 3x + 3}{x - 2}$

5. $l(x) = \dfrac{x}{x^2 - 4x}$.

Fitting a Polynomial to Data Points

Problem Statement

How many triangles can be formed by connecting n points in a plane (no three colinear)?

GRAPHING CALCULATOR SOLUTION USING LAGRANGE INTERPOLATION. One technique for solving problems is to consider simple examples of the problem and find a pattern. In this problem, the simplest case involves 3 points in a plane, and there is only one triangle. Four non-colinear points can be connected to form 4 triangles, 5 points will form 10 triangles, and 6 points will form 20 triangles.

To try to find a polynomial function that contains the given data points, we can use a method called Lagrange Interpolation. The process is simple. By finding a polynomial which contains one data point but equals zero at each of the x-coordinates of the other data points, we will have a total of n polynomials each of degree $n-1$, where n is the number of given data points. By adding these polynomials together, we have one polynomial which will pass through all of the given data points. We will use this polynomial to predict the number of triangles formed by connecting n points as in the problem above.

The data points that we want a polynomial to pass through are:

$$(3,1), (4,4), (5,10), (6,20).$$

Construct the following polynomials, each of which equals zero at three of the data points:

$$\begin{aligned} Y_1 &= (X-4)(X-5)(X-6) \\ Y_2 &= (X-3)(X-5)(X-6) \\ Y_3 &= (X-3)(X-4)(X-6) \\ Y_4 &= (X-3)(X-4)(X-5) \end{aligned}$$

When Y_1 is evaluated at $x = 4$, 5, or 6, the value is zero, but when evaluated at $x = 3$, the value is -6.

$$\begin{aligned} Y_1 &= (3-4)(3-5)(3-6) \\ &= (-1)(-2)(-3) \\ &= -6 \end{aligned}$$

We want the value at $x = 6$ to equal 1, so that the graph of Y_1 will pass through the point $(3,1)$. We will need to put a coefficient into Y_1 to make $Y_1(3) = 1$. Go back and add the coefficient $(-\frac{1}{6})$ to Y_1

$$Y_1' = -\frac{1}{6}(x-4)(x-5)(x-6)$$

In a similar manner, $Y_2(4) = 2$, $Y_3(5) = -2$, and $Y_4(6) = 6$. Inserting coefficients of 2, −5, and $\frac{10}{3}$ into Y_2, Y_3, and Y_4 respectively, we have the desired polynomials. Adding these together yields a polynomial which now passes through all the given points.

Note that there is no guarantee that the polynomial that fits through these 4 points will necessarily be the function that predicts the number of triangles that can be formed using 5 non-colinear points, but this polynomial will pass precisely through the 4 given points. A proof that this function solves our original problem would need to be done, perhaps using induction.

The polynomial that fits through the 4 data points is the sum of Y_1 through Y_4. The graph below shows the graphs of Y_1 through Y_4 on the same grid with $2 \leq x \leq 7$ and $-3 \leq y \leq 12$.

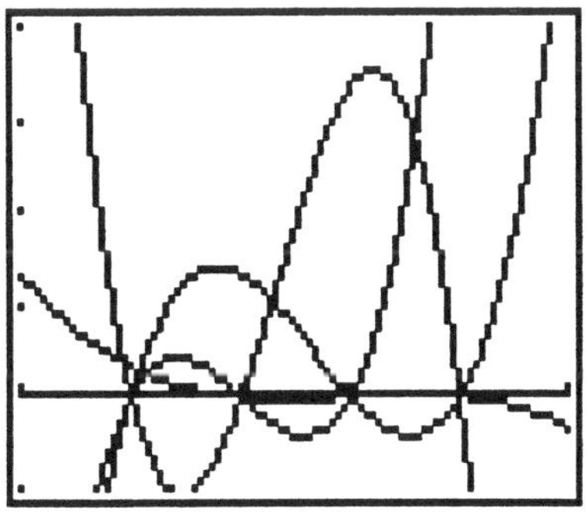

When the four functions are added together, the final function is shown below. If you graph this function using the **Integer** option under the **ZOOM** menu (press ZOOM and select **8:Integer**), the blinking trace cursor will jump to integral values. To produce a graph like the one shown here, set $X\min = -40$, $X\max = 50$, $X\text{scl} = 10$, $Y\min = -30$, $Y\max = 40$, and $Y\text{scl} = 10$.

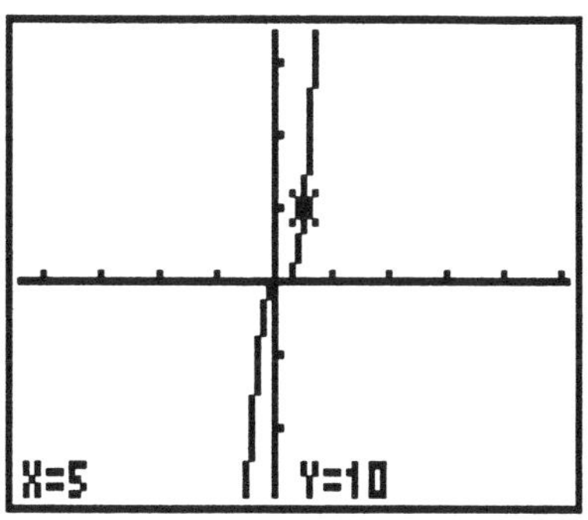

ADDITIONAL SOLUTION FOR THE TI-82. The TI-82 can also fit the least squares cubic and quartic polynomial to a set of data points. When you try to fit a cubic to four points, the result is the cubic that fits precisely through those points. The same is true for fitting a quartic through five points.

The following steps will yield the same result as in the previous example:

- Enter the ordered pairs in L_1 and L_2. (See Section 1 for entering data points).
- Press STAT, select **CALC** followed by **3:SetUp...**.
- Under **2-Var Stats** be sure that the **Xlist** contains the x-coordinates and the **Ylist** contains the y-coordinates.
- Press STAT again and select **CALC**. This time select **7:CubicReg** and press ENTER. Notice that the coefficients for the polynomial are $\frac{1}{6}$, $\frac{1}{2}$, $\frac{1}{3}$, and 0.

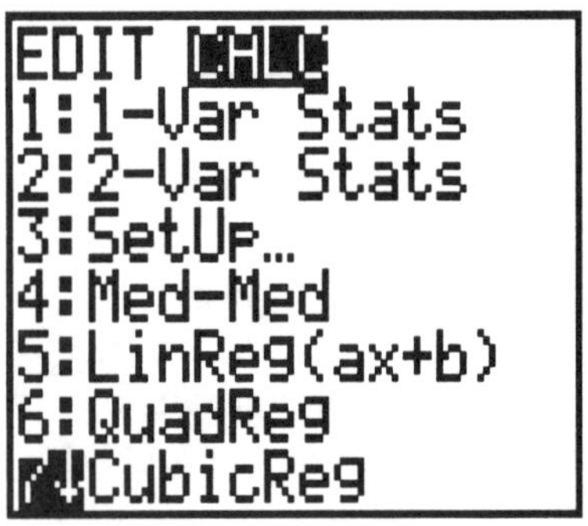

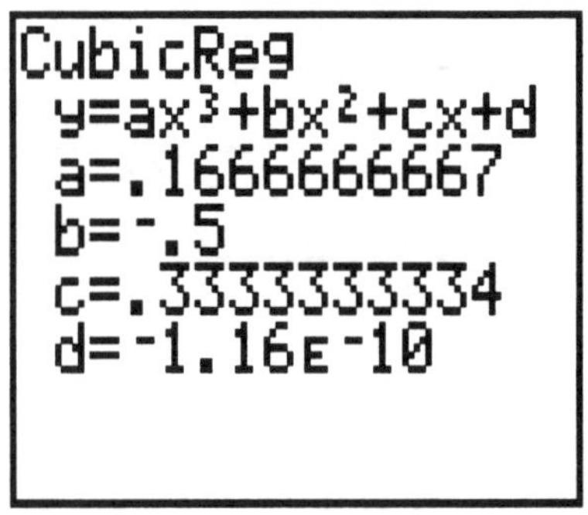

- If you want to plot the data and graph the function press Y=. Find an open function or clear a function and press VARS and select **5:Statistics.** Select **EQ** and **7:RegEQ**. Make sure all other functions are off. Now press 2nd Y= (STAT PLOT) and turn on a plot which contains the x- and y-coordinates. Press ZOOM and select **9:ZoomStat**. Tracing will follow the data points as well as the continuous model. Pressing the up and down arrows will allow you to switch from the continuous function to the discrete data points, and pressing the left and right arrows will allow you to move along the function or jump between the data points.

Additional Problem

1. An airline has terminals in n cities and would like to have at least one flight each day connecting every possible pair of cities. How many such routes are there?

SECTION 4

Exponential and Logarithmic Functions

The Naturalness of e

Problem Statement

Normally banks compound interest on a regular basis. If this is done only once a year, the *stated interest* is the true or *effective interest*. If, on the other hand, the interest is compounded more than once a year, the effective annual rate is greater than the stated rate. What happens when the interest is compounded over shorter and shorter periods of time? (The formula for compound interest appears on page 13.)

GRAPHING CALCULATOR SOLUTION.

TI-82 instructions. Press [Y=] and enter the function $f(x) = (1+.06\div x)^x$ into Y_1. Make sure all other functions are off. Press [2nd] [WINDOW] (TblSet) and set TblMin to 1 and ΔTbl to 1. Now press [2nd] [GRAPH] (TABLE). Note the Y_1 column of the table. This column gives the yearly return on $1.00 at a 6% rate. The volume in the x column gives the number of compound periods during the year. Use the down arrow to see additional return values as the number of times the interest is compounded increases. Notice that while the effective rate changes, it seems to be approaching some limit. As the length of the compounding period approaches zero and the power approaches infinity, the expression $(1 + .06 \div n)^n$ approaches a limit.

TI-81 instructions. Enter the expression $(1+.06\div 1)^1$ into the calculator and press [ENTER]. The return on $1.00 is $1.06, or a 6% rate of return. Now press the up arrow and use the left arrow to change the expression to $(1 + .06 \div 2)^2$. This will give the effect of compounding twice during the year. Press [ENTER] and notice the return. Press the up arrow and increase the number of times the interest is compounded. Notice that while the effective rate changes, it does seem to be approaching some limit. As the length of the compounding period approaches zero and the power approaches infinity, the expression $(1 + .06 \div n)^n$ approaches a limit.

Is there a simple way to arrive at this limit? To understand the limit, go back and change the .06 to 1 and repeat the process. The expression $(1+1\div n)^n$ eventually gets closer and closer to the number e. In fact, e is defined as this limit.

Now go back and enter the expression $(1+.06\div 100)^{(100\div .06)*.06}$. As you increase the number of compounding periods, what value does this expression approach? What would be another way to write this limit?

Additional Problems

1. What is the effective rate earned if the stated rate is 6% and interest is compounded monthly?

2. What is the effective rate earned if the stated rate is 8% but interest is compounded continuously?

3. Compare the function $f(x) = e^{0.06x}$ to the function in the text above, $g(x) = (1+.06\div n)^{nx}$. Graph the two for small values of n, and then for increased values of n.

Exponential and Logarithmic Functions

Problem Statement

You just won $100,000 in the lottery and you decide to deposit half of the winnings into a bank account which pays 7% compounded annually. How much will you have in the account at the end of 3 years? At the end of 20 years?

SOLUTION USING RECURSION. The calculator executes the last statement entered each time you press the [ENTER] key. Since compound interest is recursive, that is, based on the previous balance, it is easy to find with the calculator.

- Since banks truncate to 2 decimal places, the solution would be more realistic if the calculator were set to 2 decimal places. Press [MODE] and select 2 decimal places under **FLOAT**.
- Enter 50000 and press [ENTER].
- Now press [2nd] [(-)] [*] [1] [.] [0] [7] (Ans * 1.07) and press [ENTER]. This total is the balance at the end of one year.
  - Press [ENTER] again. This total is the balance at the end of 2 years.
  - Press [ENTER] again. Each time you press [ENTER] you will see the balance at the end of another year.
- Continue this process until you find the balance at the end of 20 years.

SOLUTION USING A FORMULA. The future value of a compound interest problem is given by the formula $F = 50000(1.07)^n$, where n is the number of years.

- To find the balance at the end of 3 years, press [50000] [*] [1.07] [∧] [3] [ENTER].
- To find the balance at the end of 20 years, retype the formula using 20 for the exponent. (On the TI-81, you can press the up arrow. This places a copy of the formula on the screen. Use the arrows to change the 3 to a 20 and press [ENTER].)

SOLUTION USING FUNCTIONS. The above formula for future value of a compound interest problem can be entered as a function.

- Press [Y=], select Y_1, and enter the above formula. Replace the exponent with the variable X.
- Store the value 3 as X, press [3] [STO] [X,T,θ] [ENTER]. Now press [2nd] [VARS] (Y-VARS), and select Y_1. Press [ENTER] (twice on the TI-81).
- To see the result at the end of 20 years, repeat the above process after storing 20 in X.

SOLUTION BY GRAPHING. Since we have entered the formula for compound interest as the function Y_1, we can graph the function and trace along the curve.

- Press [WINDOW] (TI-82) or [RANGE] (TI-81) and set the domain $0 \le x \le 25$ and $50000 \le y \le 200000$.
- Press [GRAPH].
- Now press [TRACE] and use the right and left arrows until you get to the points where $x = 3$ and $x = 20$. You can press [ZOOM] and [TRACE] to get increased accuracy.

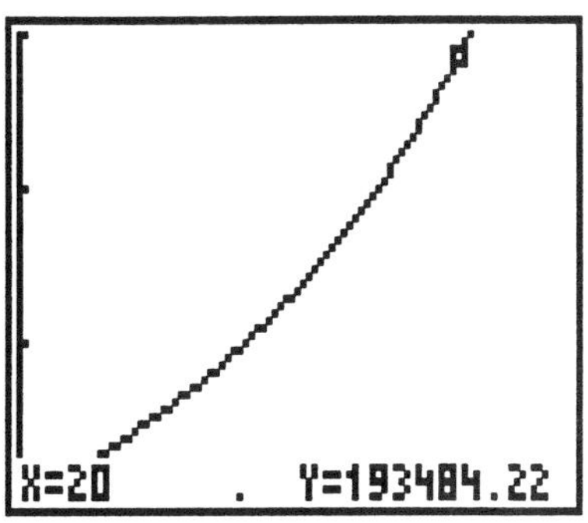

Additional Problems

1. If the $50,000 were invested at 7% compounded annually, how long would it take for the amount in the account to first go over $250,000?

2. If your parents set up an education fund for you the day you were born depositing $1700 in an account earning 10% compounded annually, how much will you have for college when you turn 18?

Annuity Problems

Problem Statement

When you start out in business for yourself, you know that you will need to set up your own retirement plan. You start out by saving $200 each month in an individual retirement account through a mutual fund which has been paying an average of 9% per year for the past 20 years. If you assume that the fund will continue to pay at the same rate, how much will you have in the account at the end of 30 years?

TI-82 GRAPHICAL SOLUTION. The TI-82 has a very nice feature for finding sequential values using recursion or iteration. This problem is a perfect example of recursion.

- First you must enter the Sequential Mode. Press [MODE] and select **Seq** from the fourth line down.

- Now press [Y=] and notice that instead of the usual Y-functions, there are two subscripted variables, U_n and V_n. To do this problem, we want to define U_n as $U_{n-1}(1.0075) + 200$. This means that each U value is $\frac{3}{4}$% of the previous value plus the $200 deposited each time. U_{n-1} can be entered by pressing [2nd] [7].

- Press [WINDOW] and notice the menu item, **FORMAT**. Press the right arrow and notice the options. For this graph we want all of the options on the left highlighted.

- To generate the U values and see the graph of these values, we must first set up the window. Press [WINDOW] and notice that there is more to this menu than there is for graphing functions. You must tell the calculator the values at which to start U, V, n, the final value of n, and the horizontal and vertical window. These are still called X and Y values, although there really are no X or Y values involved in this graph. Set the values as follows:

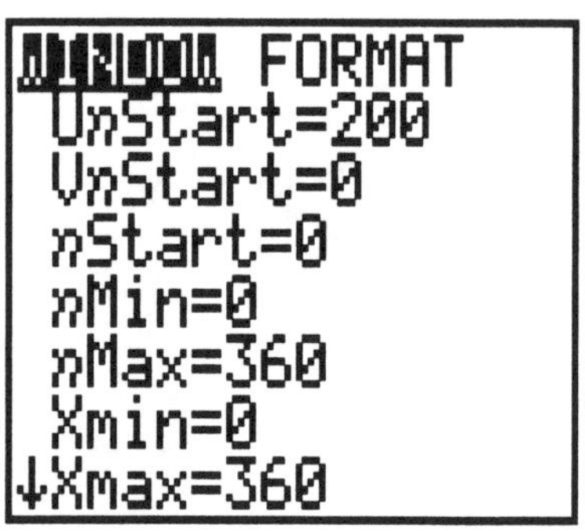

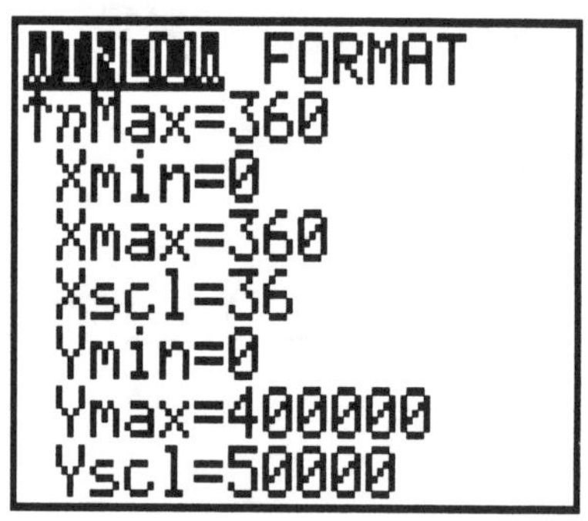

- As soon as you press GRAPH, the calculator begins to generate and plot the U values. You can press TRACE and move along the graph to see all the numerical values generated, even though there actually are not enough pixels to show all of them. On graphs of regular functions, **TRACE** only shows the functional value for the x-value of the pixels shown.
- Since tracing is rather slow, you can evaluate the recursive function at any value of n by pressing 2nd TRACE (CALC). The only menu item here is **1:value**. Press ENTER and when prompted, enter a value for n and press ENTER. A value of 359 gives the balance at the end of 360 months.

TI-82 TABLE SOLUTION. You can use the Table feature for the TI-82 to show the input and output values in tabular form. Follow the steps below:

- With the recursive function defined as above, press 2nd WINDOW (TblSet) and enter 0 for TblMin.
- Enter 36 for ΔTable, press 2nd GRAPH (TABLE) and prepare to wait. Because this function is defined recursively, output values are generated sequentially. In addition, they are not stored in the calculators memory, so whether for a graph or for a table, the calculator must regenerate the values each time you call for them. If you scroll up or down using the arrow keys to see additional values, it will again take time to generate them.

TI-81 SOLUTION. You deposit $200 into the account and it earns 0.75% (9% divided by 12) during the first month. At that point you add another $200. This process will be repeated each month for the next 360 months. The calculator will do this nicely using recursion.

- First enter 200 and press ENTER. This $200 will be stored as the last answer **ANS**.
- Now press 2nd (−), (ANS), multiply this by 1.0075, and add 200. The line should look like **Ans*1.0075+200**.
- Press ENTER. Notice that the answer is $401.50. Now each time you press ENTER, the calculator will repeat the last line entered into the calculator. After you press ENTER ten more times, you have $2501.52. This represents the total in the account as soon as you make the twelfth deposit.
- You could press ENTER 348 more times, but this is obviously not the best way to finish this problem.

PROGRAMMING SOLUTION. You can use recursion for solving this problem by writing the above steps of the graphing calculator solution into a programming loop.

Program Code: ANNUITY

Program Code	Comments
:1 →I	Initialize counter.
:Disp "NO. PAYMENTS"	
:Input J	Enter number of payments.
:Disp "AMOUNT"	
:Input D	Periodic deposit.
:D →B	Initial Balance.
:Disp "RATE"	
:Input R	Enter interest rate for the deposit period.
:Lbl 1	Begin loop.
:B*(1+R)+D →B	Add interest to balance and add deposit.
:IS>(I,J−1)	Increment I and Skip (loop back) if I is less than $J - 1$?
:Goto 1	End loop.
:Disp B	Display balance.
:End	

Store and run the program. After a short time the calculator will display the total in the account: $366,148.70.

FUNCTION SOLUTION. If we could write a single, closed-form formula or function we could compute the total in the account at the end of any given period of time without having to find the amount at the end of each previous time period. If you write the above steps and look for the pattern, you should be able to come up with the following function.

$$f(x) = \frac{(200)(1.0075^x - 1)}{0.0075}$$

- To enter this formula as one of the functions, press [Y=] and enter the formula.
- Now to store 360 in X, press 360 [STO] [X|T].
- Press [2nd] [VARS] (Y-VARS) and select the Y-variable under which you stored this function. Press [ENTER] twice.

The advantage of the function solution, in addition to being much shorter than the first two methods, is that you may easily change the function and the number of months. The first solution requires less algebra but much more time. The second solution also requires less algebra, but some programming ability. However, there are recursive functions or relations for which closed form equations are either difficult or impossible to derive. Therefore, a knowledge of the solutions using recursion is valuable.

Additional Problems

1. How much would you have in an account if you saved \$250 a month for 10 years given an annual interest rate of 9%, compounded monthly?

2. How much would you have in an account if you saved \$50 a week for 10 years given an annual interest rate of 9%, compounded each week?

3. Assume that you have retired with savings of \$750,000 and wish to pay yourself \$50,000 per year. If the balance is left to accrue interest at 8% compounded yearly, how much would you have left in 20 years? Surprised?

4. In a problem in the last section, some parents invested \$1700 in an account paying 10% compounded annually. In addition to the initial \$1700, suppose they also invest \$600 per year into the account. How much would be in the account at the end of 18 years? (**Hint.** Think carefully about the total number of payments being made.) If the interest were compounded monthly and they put \$50 per month into the account, how much would the account yield?

5. **For the TI-82 only.** Although the closed formula for the original problem is quicker (once you find or derive the formula), the following problem is much harder to do with a closed formula. However, it is very easy to do by modifying the example. Suppose you start by investing \$200 in this fund, but you plan to increase your savings by 5% per year (or $\frac{5}{12}$% per month). The only changes from the example are as follows:

   - Press [Y=] and modify U_n to be $U_n = 1.0075U_{n-1} + V_{n-1}$ and let $V_n = V_{n-1}(1 + 0.005/12)$. V_n is the amount you deposit into your savings in month n.
   - Press [WINDOW] and define $VnStart = 200$.
   - Increase the YMax on the WINDOW to 650,000 since you will obviously be saving more than before.
   - Follow the rest of the steps as above. It will be very difficult to see both the payment and the total in the fund on the same graph, but the Table feature will show both nicely.

SECTION 5

Curve Fitting: Linear Regression and Nonlinear Data

Linear Data and the Least Squares Line

Problem Statement

The serum cholesterol level in the blood is directly related to the percentage of fat calories in the diet. Given the following set of data, find the relationship.

% fat calories	9	11	14	16	22	25	31	35	38	39
cholesterol (mg/100 ml)	140	146	152	171	180	192	205	212	246	241

First plot the ordered pairs (see the earlier section on Scatter Plots). If the ordered pairs of data appear linear, you can fit the least squares line to the data and use this line to express the relationship between the level of cholesterol and the percent fat calories. The least squares line is the most common linear regression model.

TI-82 instructions. Once data points have been entered, (see Section 1), the following steps will find and plot the linear regression line over that data:

- Press STAT and select **CALC**. Select **3:SetUp...** and press ENTER. Move down to the 2-Variable Statistics and be sure that the lists containing your independent and dependent variables are highlighted. Press STAT to go back to the main Stat menu.
- Select **CALC** again from this menu and select either **5:LinReg(ax+b)** or **9:LinReg(bx+a)** to calculate the slope and intercept of the regression line.
- Press Y= select an empty function. Press VARS and choose **5:Statistics**. Move over to **EQ** and select **7:RegEQ**. The regression equation automatically will be stored in the function you selected.
- To see the residuals, store the predicted values in L3. Subtract the actual values from these values and store these residuals in L4. Now look at the scatter plot of the ordered pairs (L1,L4). (See Section 1 on Median-Median Line and Residuals for more details.)

TI-81 instructions.

- To graph the regression line, first compute the linear regression coefficients. Press [2nd] [MATRX] (STAT). The **CALC** mode will be highlighted. Select **2:LinReg** to compute the y-intercept a, the slope b, and the correlation coefficient r of the regression line. Again, press [ENTER] twice.

- Now store the regression equation as one of the four Y variables. (Select Y_3 to use in the Residual Program later.) Press [Y=] and then [VARS]. Select **LR** (Linear Regression) and **4:RegEQ** (Regression Equation). The linear regression equation will be copied onto the screen and into memory. Be sure the equal sign is highlighted and press [2nd] [CLEAR].

- Before attempting to draw the scatter plot, be sure to set the range to accommodate your data. The graph that follows has domain $5 \le x \le 45$ and range $125 \le y \le 250$.

- To see the scatter plot with the regression line, press [2nd] [MATRX] (STAT), select **DRAW** and select **2:Scatter**. Be sure to press [ENTER] after the word "Scatter" appears on the screen. The regression line will be drawn and the data points plotted. **Note.** If the data is linear or nearly linear, you may not see the data points. Because of the resolution of the screen, they may be hidden by the line. Also, your graph may vary slightly from this one if you used different settings on the calculator.

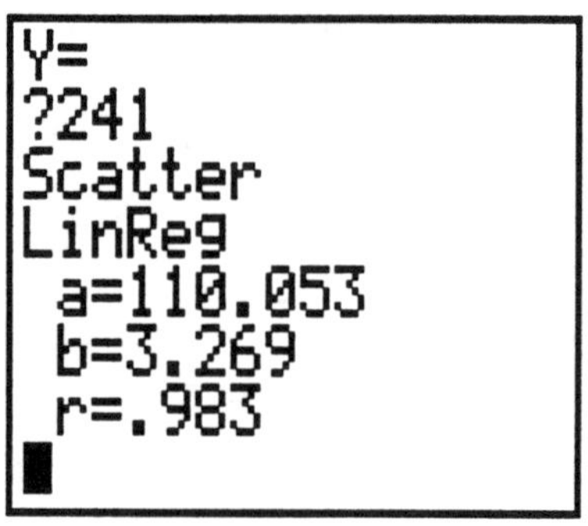

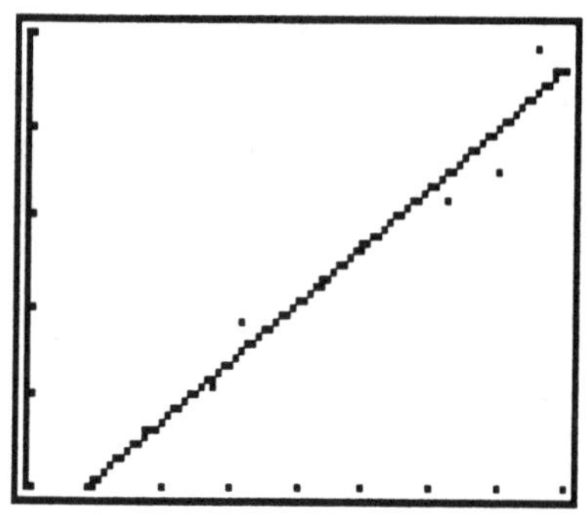

Additional Problem

1. A track is inclined at various angles and the time for a ball to roll down the trough is recorded. Plot the data and determine the relationship between the time (in seconds) and the angle of inclination (in degrees).

Angle	8	12	16	20	27	30	33	36	38	41	44
Time	2.05	1.63	1.53	1.10	0.90	0.88	0.80	0.69	0.57	0.49	0.36

   a. Use the calculator to find a linear equation which models the relationship between the angle and time.

   b. What does the slope of the linear model represent in terms of the relationship between the angle and time?

c. Use the model to predict the time for an angle of 24 degrees.

d. Using the model, estimate the angle of incline if the ball takes 1.0 second.

e. Is the model a good model? Discuss its strengths and weaknesses.

The best way to determine how well a regression line fits the data is to look at the residuals; unfortunately, many graphing calculators will not allow you do this without writing a program. If you want to use your calculator to look at the residuals, you may use the residual program in Section 1 to find residuals for the linear regression function Y_3 or use some data analysis software to study the residuals.

Scatter Plots with Transformed Data

Problem Statement

The highway patrol uses a formula for determining how fast a car in an accident was traveling, based on the length of the skid mark. The formula includes a factor for the type of road surface. If the highway department starts using a new road surface, the highway patrol needs to determine the formula for the new surface. Under controlled conditions test drivers stop cars on this surface at the following speeds and record the following skid distances.

speed in mph	20	25	30	35	45	50	55	60	65	70	80	90
skid length in feet	15	23	33	45	75	93	112	133	156	181	240	300

Calculator Solution using Linearized Data. Enter the data either directly (for the TI-82, use lists L1 for speed and L2 for the length) or by way of the data-entry/scatter-plot program and notice that the data points are not linear. As is the case with many data sets, the relationship between the variables is not linear and so the scatter plot is not linear.

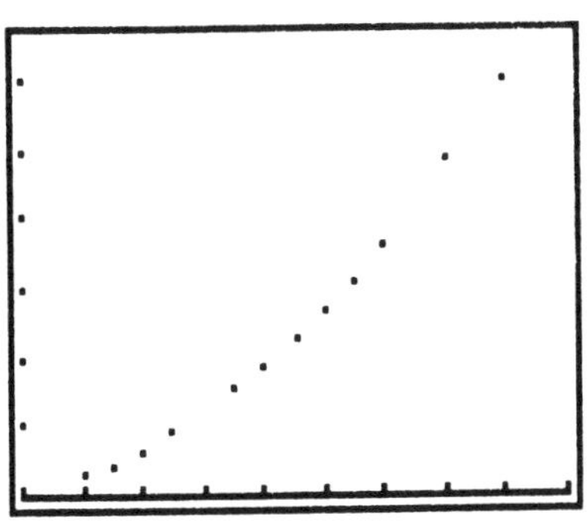

If we could linearize the data, then we could fit a line through the re-expressed data.

TI-82 instructions. It is very easy on the TI-82 to re-express data, to graph the re-expressed data, and to fit a line through the re-expressed data.

- Since this data appears to be quadratic, we want to take the square root of the y-coordinates. Press the STAT key and select **1: Edit** from the **EDIT** menu.

- Move the cursor to the top line of list L3. Be sure the L3 label is highlighted and press 2nd x^2 ($\sqrt{\ }$) followed by 2nd 2 (L2). The line at the bottom of the screen should read L3 = $\sqrt{}$L2. Now press ENTER. List L3 will be filled in with the square roots of the y-coordinates found in L2.

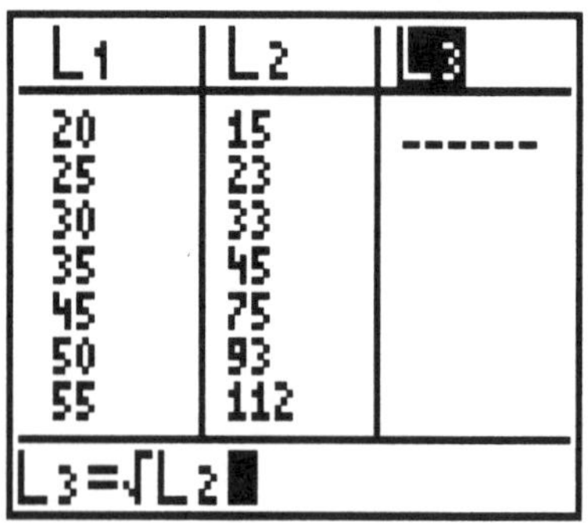

- Now set up the Stat Plot to graph L1 versus L3. Fit a line to this set of data and determine the linear relationship between the speeds and the re-expressed skid lengths. Store this relationship in Y1. The function $Y1 = -0.02489 + 0.19295x$ will fit the linearized data well while the quadratic function $Y2 = Y1^2$ should fit the original data.

- To see the graph of the final model and the original data, reset the Stat Plot for plot L1 versus L2 and turn on the function Y2. Turn off all other functions and plots.

- To see the graph of the residuals for the final model and the original data, store $Y2(L1)$ in L4, reset the Stat Plot for plot L1 versus L4 and turn off all of the functions. Press ZOOM and select **9: ZoomStat.**

TI-81 instructions. The TI-81 does not allow us to re-express data as we enter it in the **STAT** mode, so the following program will make it possible to specify two functions, one to transform the x-coordinates and one to transform the y-coordinates. The program will transform, or re-express, the data and plot the transformed data on a scatter plot.

Since this data appears to be quadratic, we could either take the square root of the y-coordinates leaving the x-coordinates alone, or square the x-coordinates while leaving the y-coordinates alone. To take the square root, press Y= and enter X for Y_1 and $\sqrt{X}$ for Y_2. Now enter and run the re-expression program.

Program Code: REEXPRES

Code	Comments
:ClrDraw	Clear the graphing window.
:All-Off	
:0 →J	
:999999 →Xmin	Place holder for Xmin.
:-999999 →Xmax	Place holder for Xmax.
:999999 →Ymin	Place holder for Ymin.
:-999999 →Ymax	Place holder for Ymax.
:Lbl 1	
:J+1 →J	
:{x}(J) →X	Stored x-data stored in X.
:Y1 →{x}(J)	X's transformed using Y_1.
:If {x}(J) < Xmin	
:{x}(J) →Xmin	Determining new Xmin.
:If {x}(J) > Xmax	
:{x}(J) →Xmax	Determining new Xmax.
:{y}(J) →X	Stored y-data stored in X.
:Y2 →{y}(J)	Y's transformed using Y_2.
:If {y}(J) < Ymin	
:{y}(J) →Ymin	Determining new Ymin.
:If {y}(J) > Ymax	
:{y}(J) →Ymax	Determining new Ymax.
:If J< Dim{x}	
:Goto 1	
:.1abs(Xmax−Xmin) →Xscl	Transforming the domain.
:Xmin − Xscl →Xmin	
:Xmax + Xscl →Xmax	
:.1abs(Ymax − Ymin) →Yscl	Transforming the range.
:Ymin − Yscl →Ymin	
:Ymax + Yscl →Ymax	
:Scatter	Drawing the scatter plot.
:End	

- After the program is entered, press the [2nd] key followed by the [CLEAR] key. This stores the program.
- The program will also transform the domain and range using the same transformation.

- We are now ready to run this program. Press the PRGM key and either arrow down to this program or press the program number or letter. Press ENTER and the program will transform the data and plot the new scatter plot.

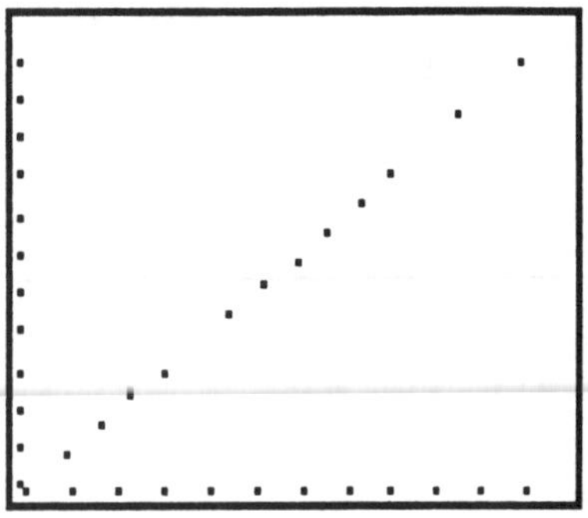

- Since the data was quadratic, the re-expression did linearize the data. We can now fit the least squares line through these re-expressed points using linear regression. The equation for the re-expressed y-coordinate is $y = -0.02489 + 0.19295x$. These coefficients are the slope and intercept of the linear regression line rounded to 5 decimal places. This line fits the linear data, so $y = (-0.02489 + 0.19295x)^2$ should fit the original data. The figure on the left shows the data restored to its original form. The figure on the right shows the fit of the model (function) to the data.

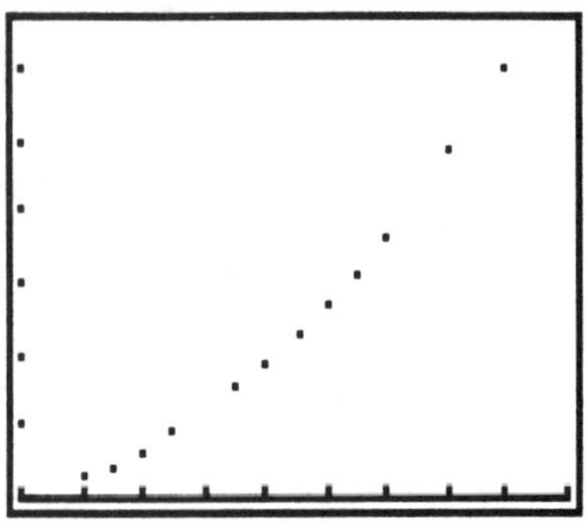

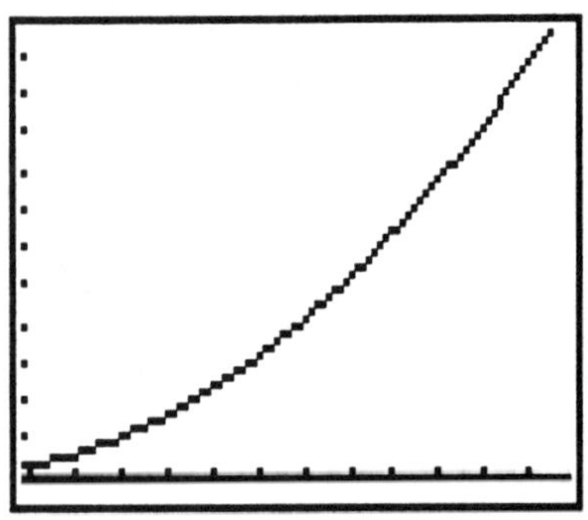

- In order to determine if the fit is as good as it looks, we need to examine the residuals. With the function $y = (-0.02489 + 0.19295x)^2$ stored as Y_3, running the **RESIDUAL** program produces the following results. The figure on the left shows the residuals while the figure on the right shows the range of these residuals. Actual results will vary depending on whether or not you round the coefficients before graphing.

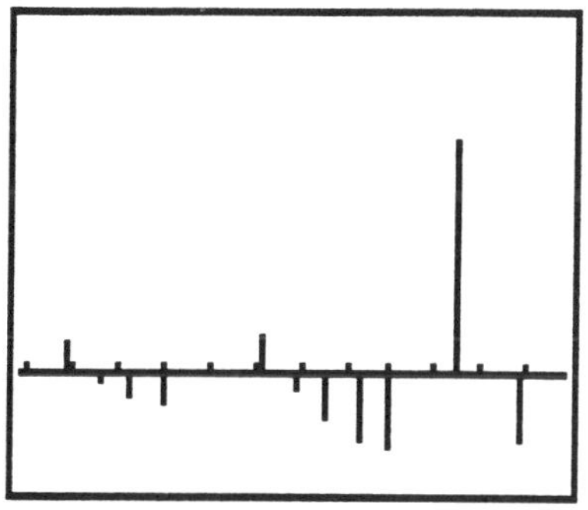

Additional Problems

1. The cost of going to college is rising faster than the general cost of living. The following table gives the Consumer Price Index (one measure of the cost of living) and the average cost (tuition and fees) for both public and private colleges over the past 10 years. Find exponential models for the CPI, the cost of public colleges and the cost of private colleges as functions of time and compare the rates of growth.

Year	1981	1982	1983	1984	1985
CPI	90.9	96.5	99.6	103.9	107.6
Public	909	1031	1148	1228	1318
Private	4113	4639	5093	5556	6121
Year	1986	1987	1988	1989	1990
CPI	109.6	113.6	118.3	124.0	130.7
Public	1414	1537	1646	1781	1809
Private	6658	7116	7722	8446	9391

2. The rate at which oxygen is consumed by animals, in ml/sec, is related to the animal's body mass. Several representative data points are given in the following table.

Mass (kg)	.006	.03	1.1	3.1	5.2	10.3	30.0	100	170	300
Oxygen (ml/sec)	.016	.058	1.08	2.50	3.80	6.61	15.7	41.7	64.1	101

a. Plot the data and determine the nature of the relationship between the oxygen rate and body mass.

b. Find a relationship which linearizes the data.

c. Fit a line through the linearized data and determine the slope and intercept.

d. Find a model which approximates the original data.

SECTION 6

Trigonometry

Toolkit of Trigonometric Functions

Problem Statement

Most periodic phenomena can be modeled by some form of the basic trigonometric functions. The basic sine function forms a sinusodial wave, and all of the other trigonometric functions can be defined in terms of the sine function. The tides, electrical currents, temperature, and daylight cycles are all examples of phenomena that can be modeled by sine waves. Let's investigate the basic trigonometric functions on the calculator.

GRAPHING CALCULATOR INVESTIGATIONS. The basic sine wave function has period 2π and amplitude 1. The calculator has a special graphing window for trigonometric functions. Press the [Y=] key followed by [SIN] and [X,T,θ]. Be sure that all the other functions are clear or turned off. Now press the [ZOOM] key and select **7**, the **ZTrig** or **Trig** window option. Two cycles of the graph of the sine function will be drawn.

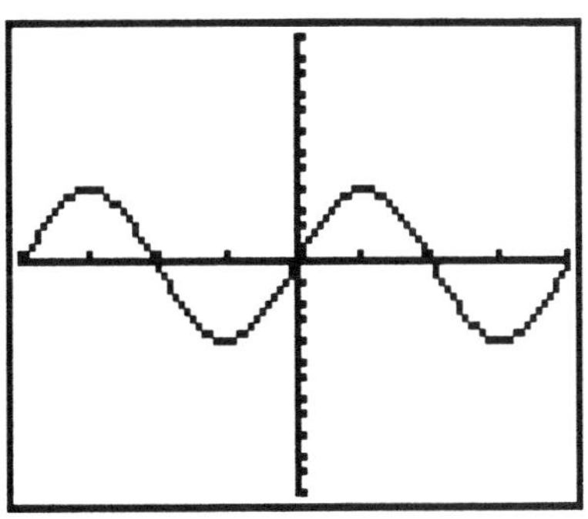

At this point go back and enter the cosine as function Y_2. Press GRAPH to see the graph of both the sine and cosine. Notice that the cosine looks exactly like the sine, except that it is shifted horizontally.

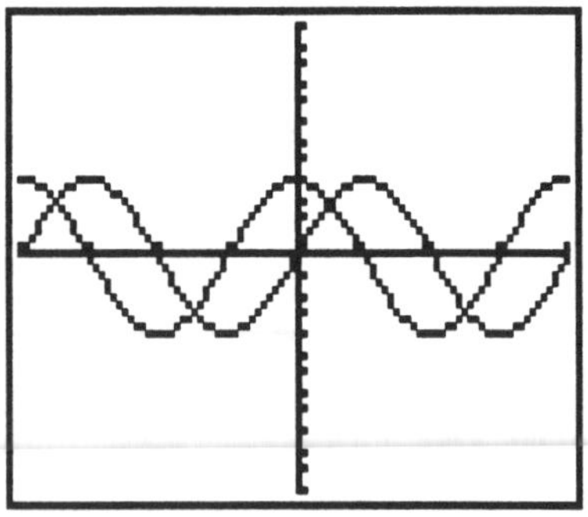

It appears that the cosine is simply the sine shifted to the left by one-fourth of a cycle, or $\frac{\pi}{2}$. Enter $\sin(x + \frac{\pi}{2})$ as function Y_3. Press GRAPH and notice that the cosine equals the $\sin(x + \frac{\pi}{2})$.

The other four trigonometric functions are combinations of the sine and/or cosine. The tangent is the ratio of the sine to the cosine. Go back and replace Y_3 with $\sin(x) \div \cos(x)$ and press GRAPH. Notice where the tangent is zero, where it equals 1, and where it is undefined.

Repeat the above process with $Y_3 = \cos X \div \sin X$. This ratio is defined as the cotangent. It is, of course, the reciprocal of the tangent. The secant is simply the reciprocal of the cosine.

Let $Y_3 = 1 \div \cos X$ and graph Y_3. Notice the range, where the function equals the cosine, and where it is undefined. Now repeat this process with the reciprocal of the sine. The resulting function is called the cosecant.

The Sine and Cosine as Circular Functions

Problem Statement

The sine and cosine functions can be defined as the coordinates of points on the unit circle. The argument or independent variable of both functions is the distance in a counter-clockwise direction along the circumference of the unit circle from the point (1,0). If this distance value is paired with the first coordinate of the point on the unit circle, the cosine function is formed. If the second coordinate of the point on the unit circle is paired with the distance, the resulting ordered pairs form the sine function.

GRAPHING CALCULATOR SIMULATION. The parametric graphing capabilities of the calculator can be used to show the relationship between the points on the unit circle and the sine and cosine functions. The following procedure will draw both the unit circle and the graph of the sine or cosine function. Follow the steps below to see this relationship.

- Press the MODE key and select the **Par** or **Param** feature. Use the arrow keys to move to this option and press ENTER. From the same screen select the **Simul** key so that the unit circle and the circular functions will be drawn simultaneously.
- Now press Y= and for X_{1T} enter $\cos T$. For Y_{1T} enter $\sin T$; for X_{2T} enter T; for Y_{2T} enter $\sin T$. Be sure that X_{3T} and Y_{3T} are clear.
- In order to plot the unit circle and the sine or cosine, we need to set the ranges for X, Y, and T. Press the WINDOW or RANGE key and set the parameters as follows:

$$\begin{aligned} T\min &= 0 \\ T\max &= 6.29 \\ T\text{step} &= .05 \\ X\min &= -1 \\ X\max &= 6.29 \\ X\text{scl} &= 1 \\ Y\min &= -2.5 \\ Y\max &= 2.5 \\ Y\text{scl} &= 1 \end{aligned}$$

- Press 2nd and PRGM (DRAW) and select **1:ClrDraw** to clear any previous graphs. Be sure to press ENTER after selecting the clear draw option. Now press GRAPH. Notice that as the unit circle is plotted, the sine function is also plotted. Each y-coordinate of the sine function is the same as the y-coordinate of the point on the unit circle.
- Press the TRACE key and notice the value of the parameter T and the values of x and y. The value of T is the radian measure, or distance around the unit circle, the value of x is the cosine for that value of T, and the value of y is the sine. The up arrow will yield the corresponding point on the

graph of the sine function. Here the value of T and x will be the same and the value of y will be $\sin(x)$.

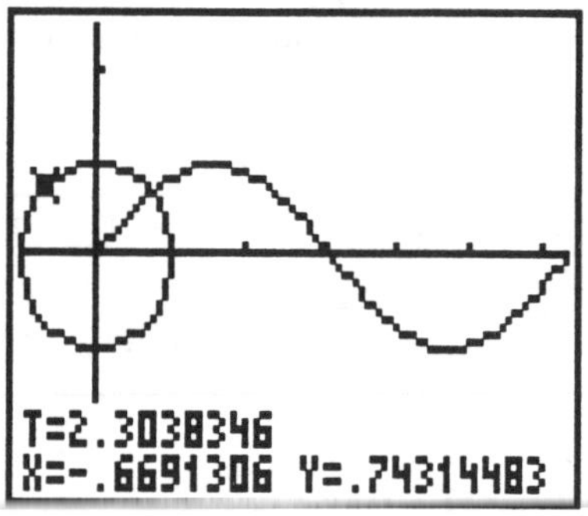

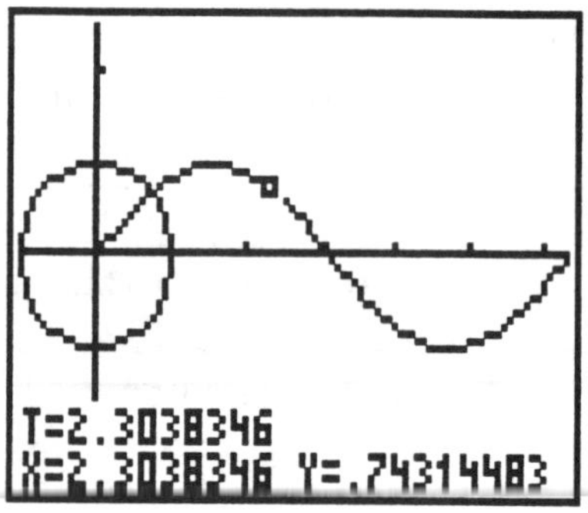

- To see the unit circle and the cosine graphed simultaneously, go back and change Y_{2T} to cos T, and repeat the above steps. In the figures below it is more difficult to see that the y-coordinate of the cosine on the left is the same as the x-coordinate of the point on the unit circle in the figure on the right. Use the TRACE key and the arrows to again see the relationship between the unit circle and the cosine function.

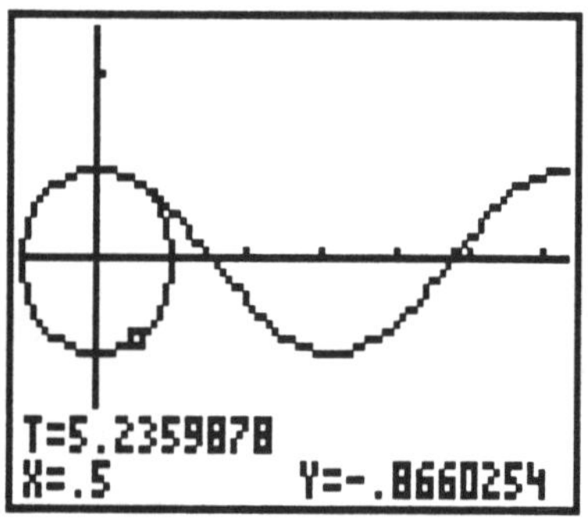

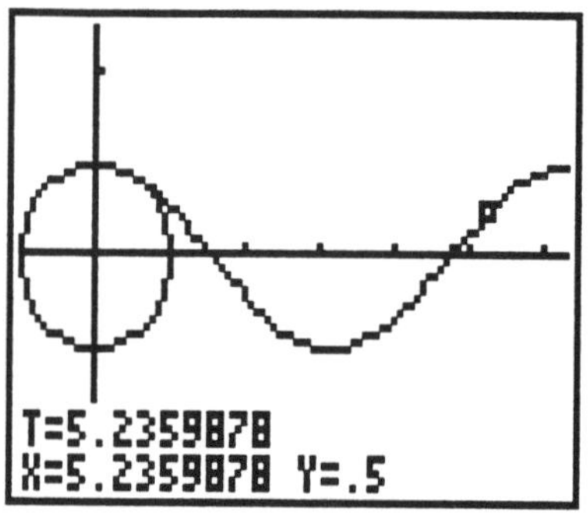

Advanced Graphing Lab

Problem Statement

Lets observe the transformations of functions formed by adding and multiplying by constants. Then, in the second part of the lab, we'll observe what happens when we add and multiply functions.

GRAPHING CALCULATOR SOLUTION. Use your calculator to investigate the following. Make notes and draw conclusions.

- Graph $y = A\sin(x)$. Store various values in A and note the effect the A has on the graph of $y = \sin(x)$.
- Graph $y = \sin(Bx)$. Since this function is periodic, it is easy to see what effect B has on the graph. Discuss this transfomation.
- Graph the function $y = \cos(x - C)$. Store various values in C and note the effect C has on the graph of the normal cosine function.
- Graph the function $y = x\sin(x)$. What effect does the x have on the graph of $y = \sin(x)$? Graph $y = x$ and $y = -x$ on the same axes with $y = x\sin(x)$. What do you notice?
- Graph $y = 2 + \sin(x)$. What effect does adding 2 have on the graph of $y = \sin(x)$.
- Now graph $y = x + \sin(x)$. Explain the effect of adding the x to $\sin(x)$. Now graph $y = x$ on the same axes as $y = x + \sin(x)$. Make some generalizations about the effect of adding functions.
- Use the conclusions from above to sketch graphs of $y = x\cos(x)$, $y = |x| + \sin(x)$ and $y = e^x + \sin(x)$. Use your calculator to check your graphs.

Additional Problems

1. The approximate hours of sunlight in Durham, North Carolina for the 21st of each month are given in the following table. Find a sine curve which predicts the hours of sunlight for any given day of the year.

Month	Jan.	Feb.	Mar.	Apr.	May	June
Sunlight	10.08	11.06	12.18	13.34	14.22	14.65
Month	July	Aug.	Sept.	Oct.	Nov.	Dec.
Sunlight	14.20	13.33	12.20	11.04	10.09	9.68

2. Alternating electrical current can be modeled by a sine function. Write the function for an alternating current with a frequency (the reciprocal of the period) of 60 Hz (60 cycles per second) and an amplitude of 220. Graph the function over 2 cycles.

3. To create waves with various shapes in producing electronic music, a process called FM feedback is used. A wave is produced, fed back into the function and this new signal is then fed back into the function again. Graph the function $f(x) = \sin(2x)$ and $g(x) = \sin(x + f(x))$. Now graph $g(g(x))$ and $g(g(g(x)))$. What shape does the wave seem to be approaching?

SECTION 7

Matrices

Matrix Operations

Problem Statement

The Burger Barn has two stores in Durham. Both stores sell three types of sandwiches: hamburgers, chicken fillets, and fish fillets.

In September, Store I sold 512 hamburgers, 209 chicken sandwiches, and 52 fish sandwiches. Store II sold 491 hamburgers, 192 chicken sandwiches, and 48 fish sandwiches. In October, Store I sold 623 hamburgers, 231 chicken sandwiches, and 72 fish sandwiches. Store II sold 578 hamburgers, 203 chicken sandwiches, and 62 fish sandwiches.

Store I charges \$1.89, \$1.79, and \$1.59 respectively for burgers, chicken, and fish. Store II is located in an expensive mall, and its prices are higher: \$1.95, \$1.85, and \$1.65.

What was the total number of each type of sandwich sold during the two months by each store? What was the change in the number sold of each type of sandwich? How much revenue did each store receive from selling sandwiches each month?

CALCULATOR MATRIX SOLUTION. While this problem could be solved by arithmetic, the data can be organized nicely and all of the questions answered using matrices.

- Press [MATRIX] and select **EDIT**. Select **1: [A]**. Change the dimension of matrix A to 2 by 3. Press [2] [ENTER] [3] and [ENTER]. You are now ready to enter the first piece of data in the first row, first column of matrix A. Let the row stand for the store number, and the columns for the types of sandwiches. Enter 512, 209, and 52 in the first row and 491, 192, and 48 in row 2. For the TI-81, you have to press [2nd] [clear] to store this data in matrix A. For the TI-82, press [2nd] [MODE] (QUIT) to return to the main screen.

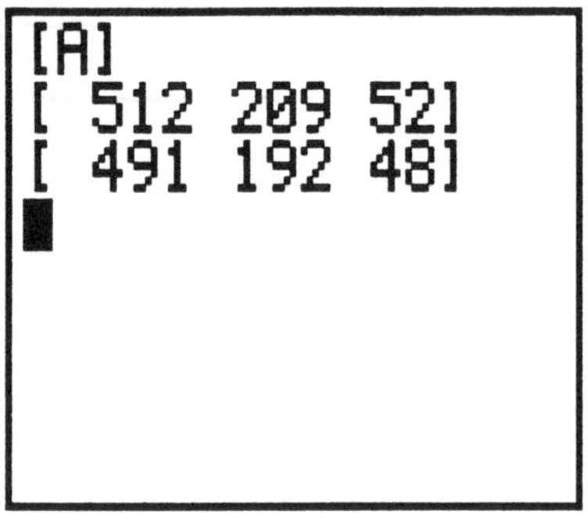

- Repeat the above steps, this time selecting **2:** [**B**] , and enter the appropriate data by rows. This data will be stored in matrix B.

- To find the total number of each type of sandwich sold during the two months, we need to add entries. To do this press [MATRIX] [1] ([A]) [+] [MATRIX] [2] ([B]) on the TI-82, or [2nd] [1] ([A]) [+] [2nd] [2] ([B]) [ENTER] on the TI-81. The resulting 2 by 3 matrix will be the total for each sandwich by store. To see the entire matrix, set the mode so that there are zero decimal places (press [MODE], arrow down to **Float**, arrow over to **0**, press [ENTER]), then you will be able to see the entire matrix. Otherwise it may be necessary to use the right arrow to see the second and third columns of the matrix.

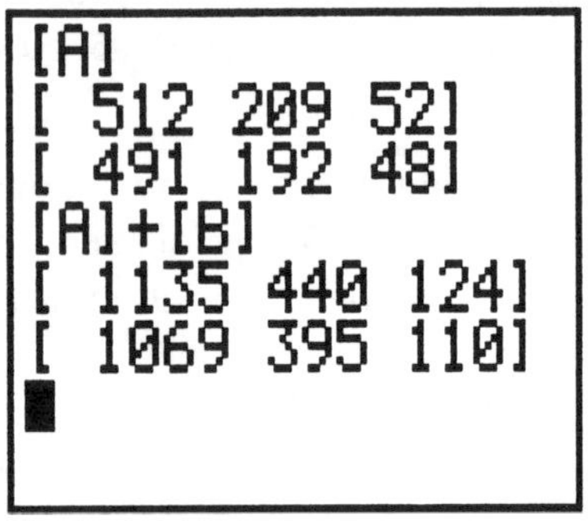

- To find the change from September to October, press [MATRIX] [2] ([B]) [−] [MATRIX] [1] ([A]) or [2nd] [2] ([B]) [−] [2nd] [1] ([A]) [ENTER]. The resulting 2 by 3 matrix shows the change in the number of sandwiches by store.

```
[ 491  192 48]
[A]+[B]
[ 1135 440 124]
[ 1069 395 110]
[B]-[A]
[ 111  22 20]
[ 87   11 14]
```

- To find the total revenue from sandwiches, it is necessary to store the price data in a 3 by 2 matrix. Since prices include dollars and cents, use 2 decimal places. Press MODE, arrow down to **Float**, arrow over to **2**, ENTER. Enter the hamburger prices in the first row, the chicken prices in row 2, and the fish prices in row 3 of matrix C. Now multiply matrix $([A] + [B])$ by C. The resulting 2 by 2 matrix has the desired information plus some extraneous information. What does the entry in row 1 column 2 give us? Row 2 column 1?

```
[ 87   11 14]
([A]+[B])*[C]
[ 3129.91 3231.…
[ 2902.36 2996.…
([A]+[B])*[C]
…129.91 3231.85]
…902.36 2996.8 ]
```

Powers of Square Matrices

Problem Statement

Planning for your eventual retirement, you decide to put the $10,000 your rich aunt gave you for graduation into a mutual fund and you further plan to put an additional $100 each month into the fund. This fund has historically yielded an average return of 9% per year (0.0075 per month.) How much would you have in the account at the end of one year? At the end of 30 years?

Calculator Matrix Solution. While this problem is usually not done with matrices, the matrix solution is nice. Annuity problems involve adding and multiplying, exactly the operations in matrix multiplication.

- Press MODE, arrow down to **Float**, arrow over to **2**, ENTER.
- Define matrix C to be a 1 by 2 matrix with entries [10000 100] and matrix B as a 2 by 2 matrix with 1.0075 and 0 in the first row and two 1's in the second row.
- Multiply matrix C by B. How did the first entry get to be $10175? What does this quantity represent?

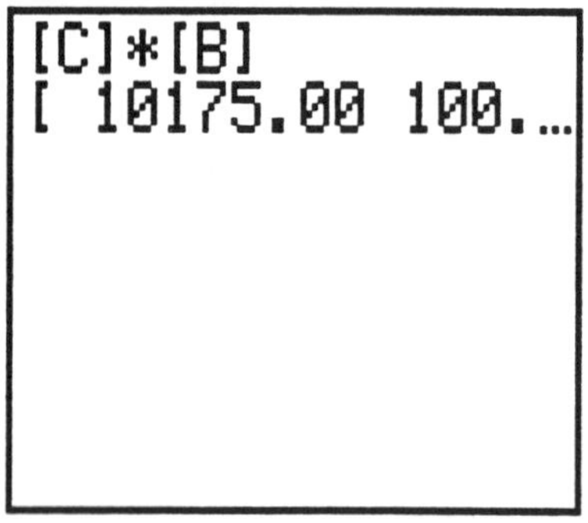

- One way to find the amount at the end of 12 months, is to press 2nd (-) * MATRIX 2 (ANS * [B]) followed by ENTER. This will yield the total in the account after the second installment of $100. Now each time you press ENTER, you will get a matrix with the total amount in the account after an additional installment. After pressing ENTER 10 additional times, the last line will indicate the total after 12 installments.

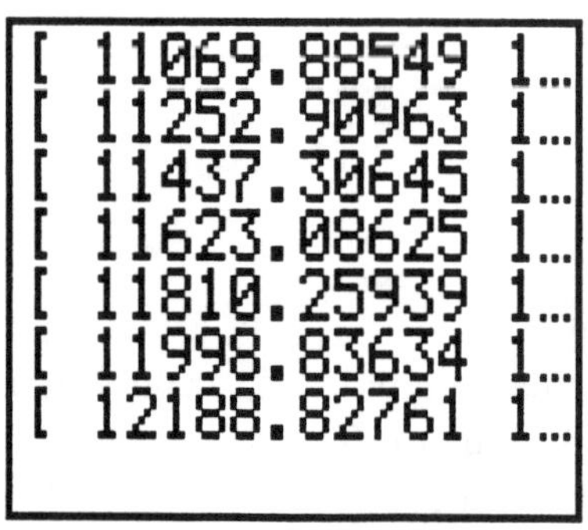

- To find the total in the account after 360 months, you can press [ENTER] 348 more times, or raise matrix B to the 360th power and then left-multiply by matrix C. Unfortunately, the TI-81 will not raise a matrix to a power (other than powers of 2). See the program following the TI-82 instructions.

TI-82 instructions. The TI-82 has the ability to take any power (up to 250) of a square matrix. The annuity problem can be solved very simply now with the following additional step:

- Press [MATRIX] [3] ([C]). Now press [×] followed by [MATRIX] [2] ([B]) [∧] [1] [8] [0] [×] [MATRIX] [2] ([B]) [∧] [1] [8] [0] (that is, $[C] * [B] \wedge 180 * [B] \wedge 180$). Notice that you have saved over $330,000.

  Note: Since the TI-82 will only raise a matrix to the 250th power, we use 180 + 180 to get 360. You could have used any other sum of powers to get 360 as long as both were less than 250.

PROGRAMMING SOLUTION. The following program will raise a square matrix B to an integral power. Before running the program, be sure to enter the matrix B as defined above. Enter [10000 100] into matrix C.

Program Code: MATPOW

Program Code	**Comments**
:1 →J	
:Disp "POWER"	
:Input N	Input the desired power.
:[B]	Stores Matrix B as ANS.
:If N ≤ 1	
:Goto 2	
:Lbl 1	
:Ans[B]	Multiply Ans by $[B]$ N times.
:IS>(J,N−1)	Increment J until J equals N.
:Goto 1	
:Lbl 2	
:Ans →[A]	Store Ans in Matrix $[A]$.
:Disp [A]	
:End	

Now run the program and at the "POWER" prompt, enter 360 and press ENTER. Follow this by 2nd 3 × 2nd 1, ([C] * [A]) ENTER. Does the amount in the first row, first column surprise you?

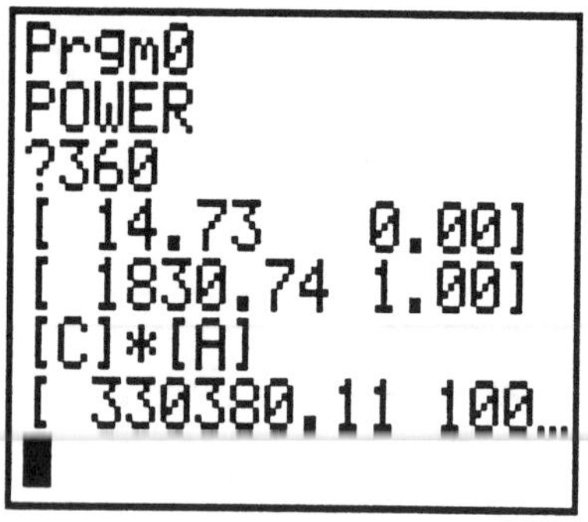

Additional Problems

1. Assume that at age 60 you retire and have managed to save $500,000. The account your money is in pays a 6% annual rate, compounded monthly. Being optomistic, you wish to withdraw the same amount each month from the account for the next 40 years. How much can you withdraw each month?

2. Upon reflection, you realize that inflation will cause your money to be worth less in the future, so you plan to withdraw a certain amount each month, and have that amount increase with inflation. You assume a 2% annual inflation rate.

   a. Now how much can you take out the first month?

   b. How much will you withdraw at age 100?

SECTION 8

Programming Hints

Programming Hints for the Texas Instruments TI-82 and TI-81

The following hints will acquaint you with the basic mechanics for writing programs. These hints are intended to teach simply the mechanics used to enter a program, rather than programming logic.

To write a program, follow these steps:

- Press the [PRGM] key.
- The screen will look something like this:

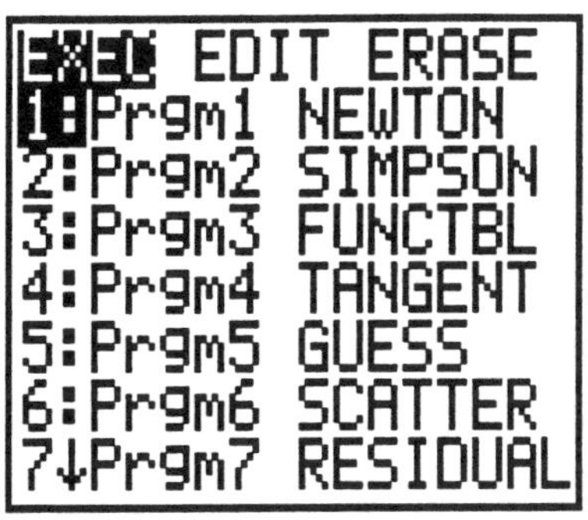

- When the **EXEC** is selected, the listing of programs is displayed. You may arrow down to the program you wish to run, or select the program number or letter.
- For the TI-82, press the [▷] key to highlight **NEW**. Select **1:Create New**. For the TI-81, press the [▷] key to highlight **EDIT**. If there is a title for the existing program, press the [▽] key until you find an available program space, then press [ENTER].

The TI-81's third menu can be used to see the memory taken up by each program and to erase individual programs. On the TI-82, use [2nd] [+] (MEM) and select **2:Delete** then **6:Prgm** to erase programs.

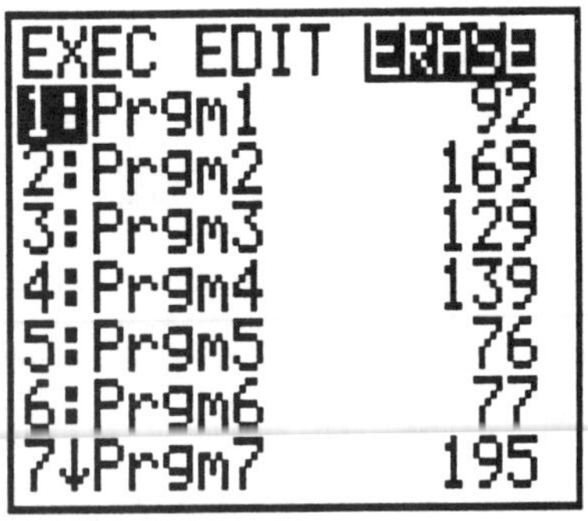

You are now ready to enter the program.

At the "Name =" or "Prgm:" prompt, type in a title for the program of up to 8 letters and press [ENTER].

Program statements are found under the **PRGM** menu. When you press [PRGM] from the **EDIT** mode, you will notice a different menu. With the **CTL** highlighted, the menu looks like this:

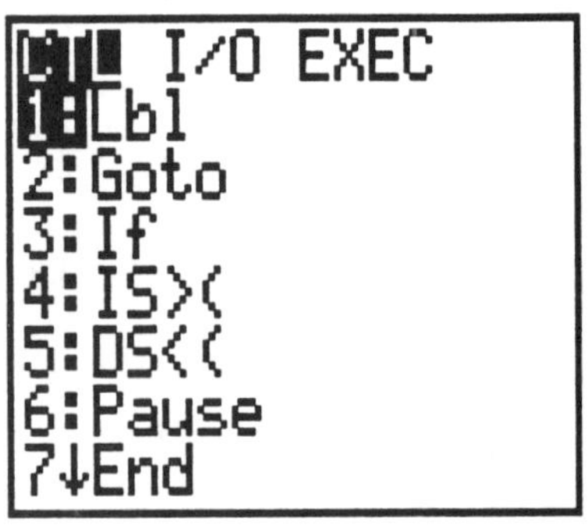

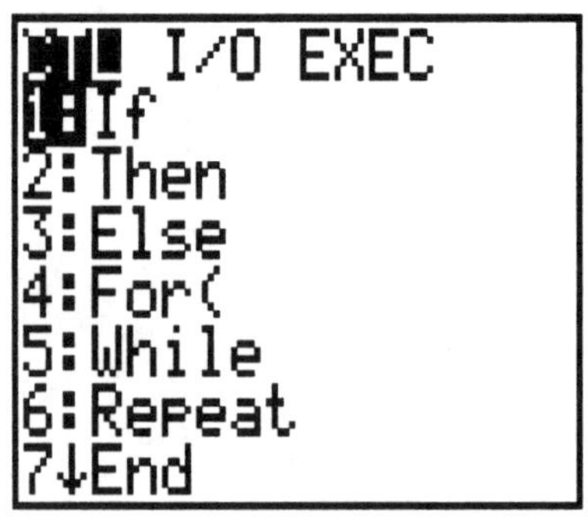

Like the **CTL** menu, **I/O**, the Input/Output menu, can only be accessed in the program edit mode:

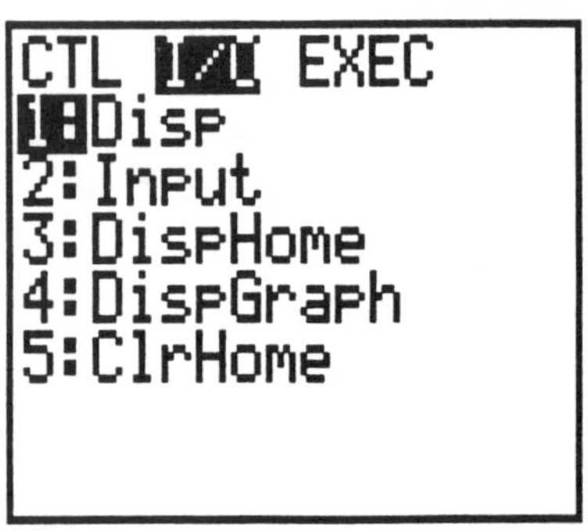

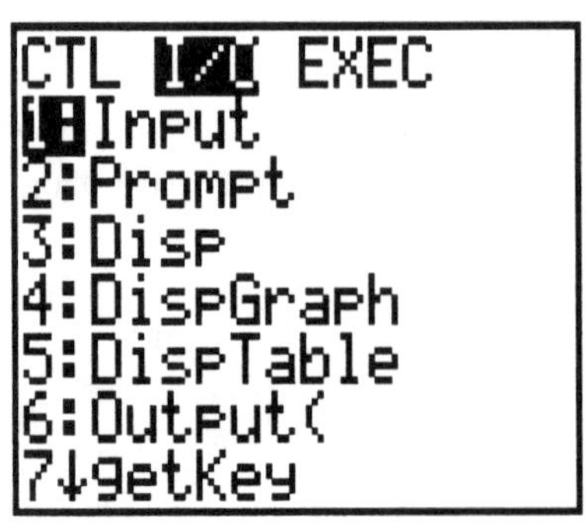

Other symbols and commands are written into programs by pressing the same keys you would to activate the symbol or command in the normal execution mode. You will find programming easier if you are familiar with the keyboard and menus. Most of the symbols look just as they do on the keys or in the menus. The [STO▷] key produces the → symbol used to store or assign a value to a variable.

Many of the commands needed to program are found in the various menus. All of these menus, with the exception of the **CTL** and **I/O** menus can be used either in or out of programming mode. The menus are listed below for your convenience.

MATH/TEST MENUS: The Math menu has 4 submenus: **MATH**, **NUM**, **HYP**, and **PRB**. These menus may look different on the TI-81.

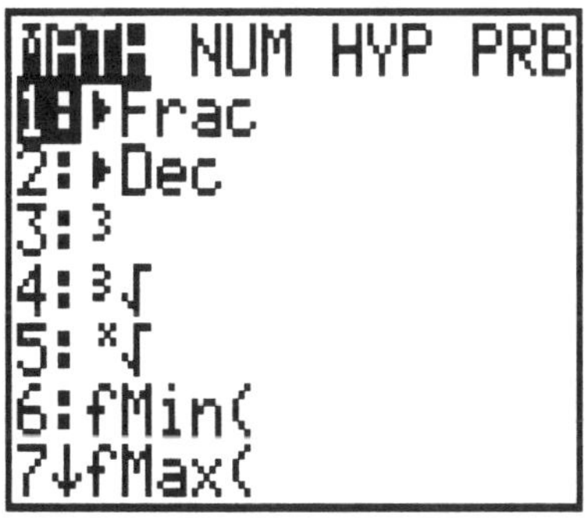

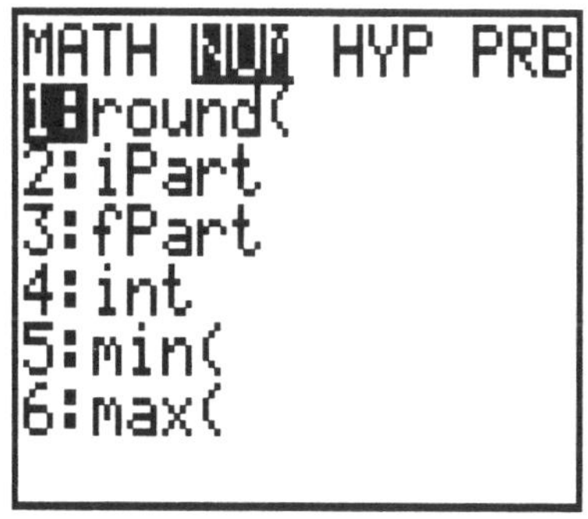

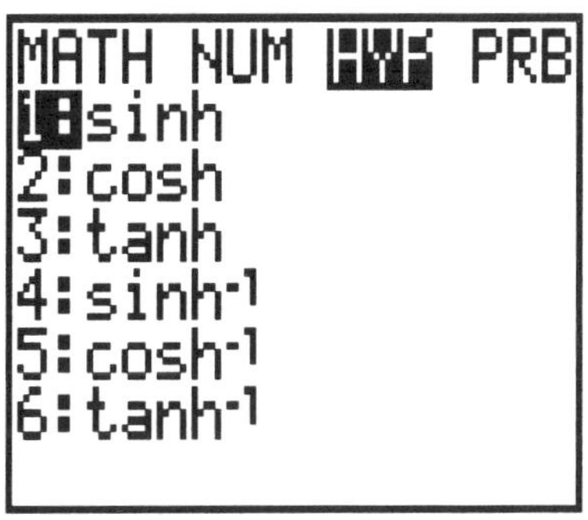

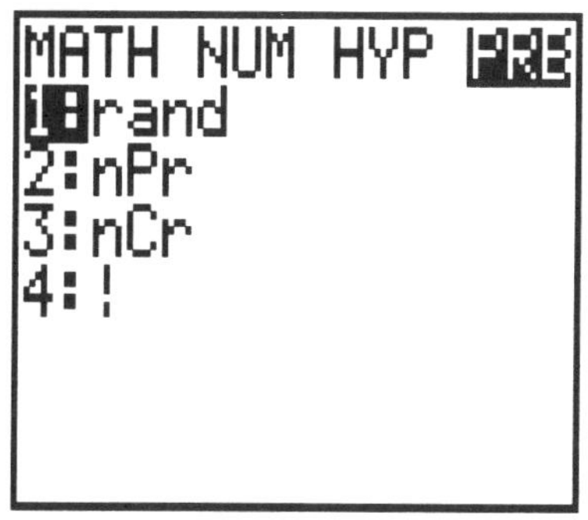

The second menu under this key is the **TEST** menu which contains the relationship symbols needed for decisions in programs.

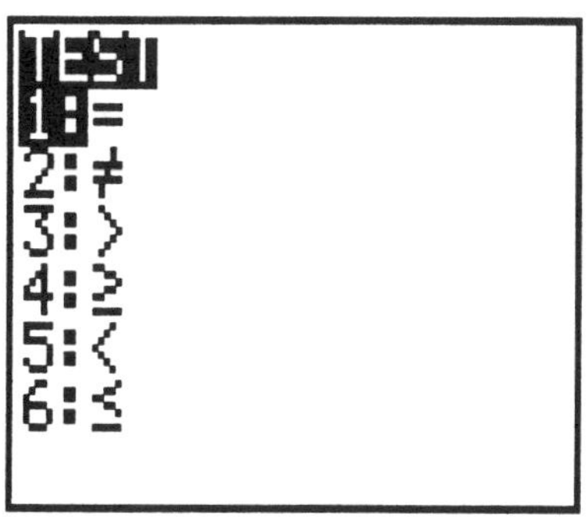

MATRIX/STAT MENUS: The **MATRIX** menu has 2 or 3 submenus:

TI-82:

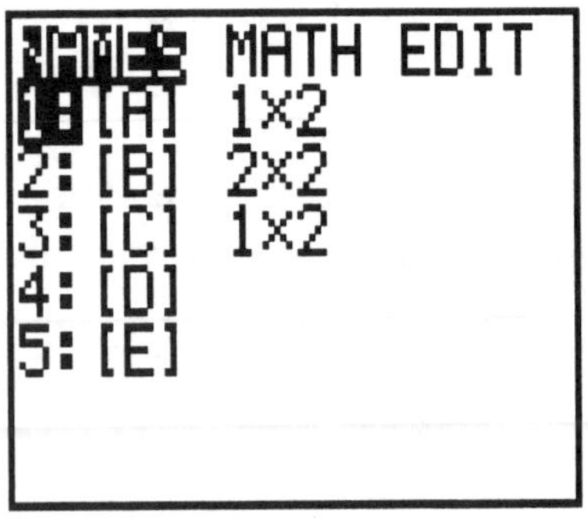

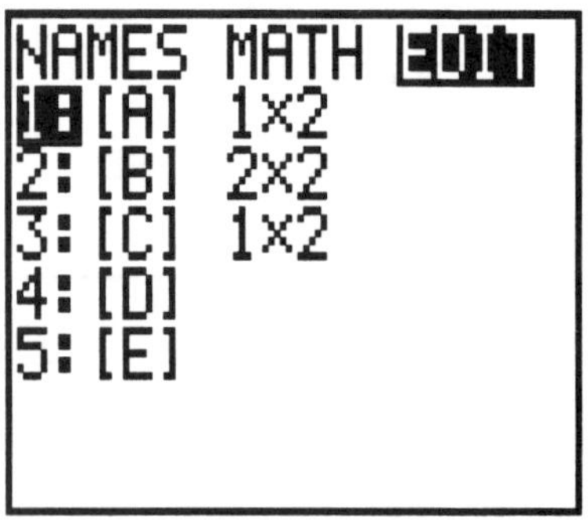

TI-81:

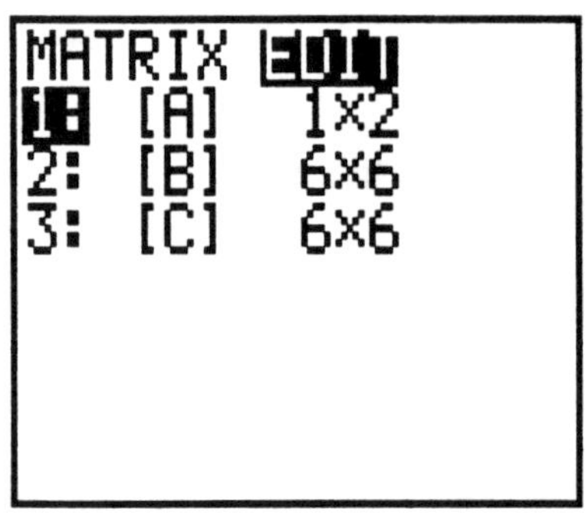

The **STAT** menu contains the following submenus:

TI-82:

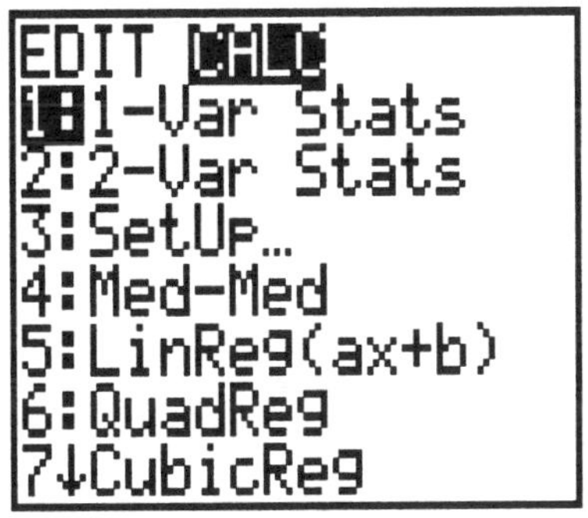

TI-81:

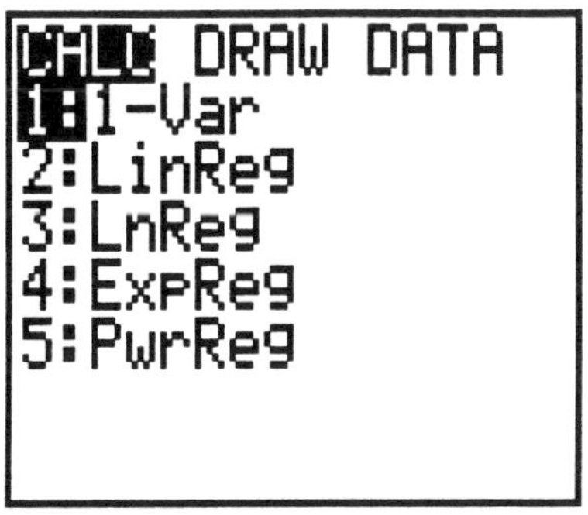

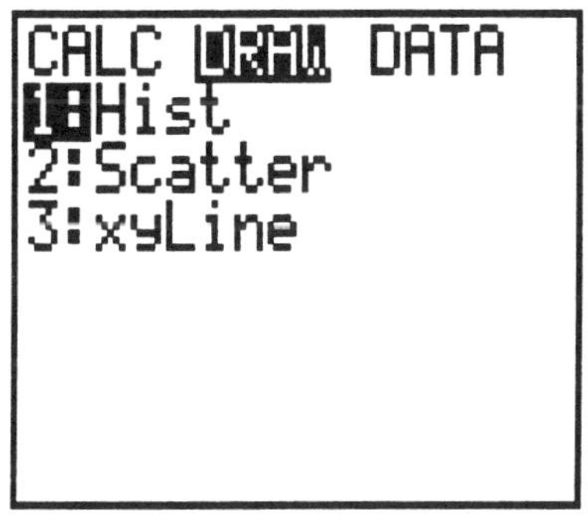

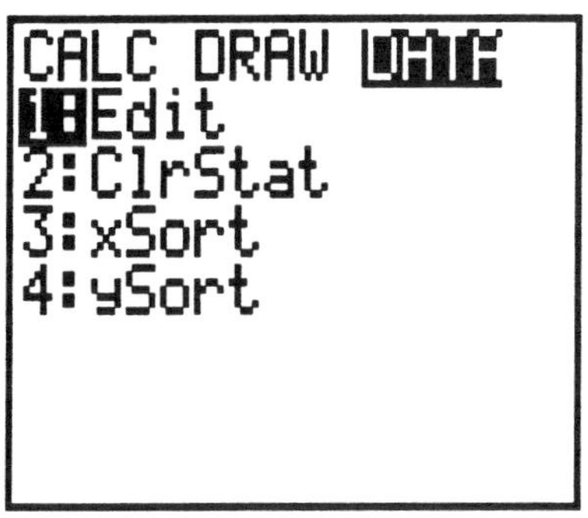

PRGM/DRAW MENUS: The **PRGM** menus are shown at the beginning of this section. The second menu under this key is the **DRAW** menu. On the TI-81, only the first submenu is available.

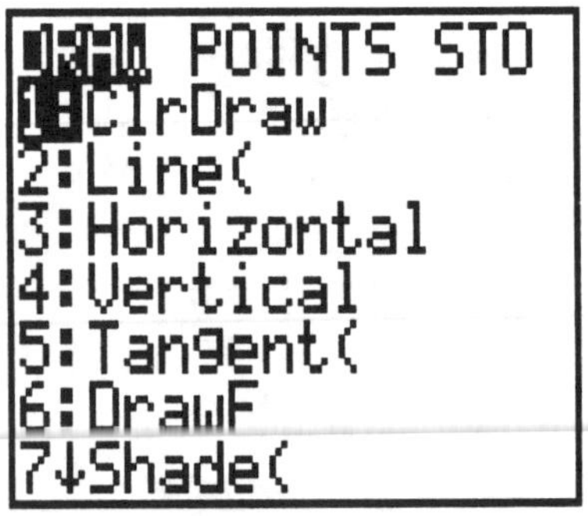

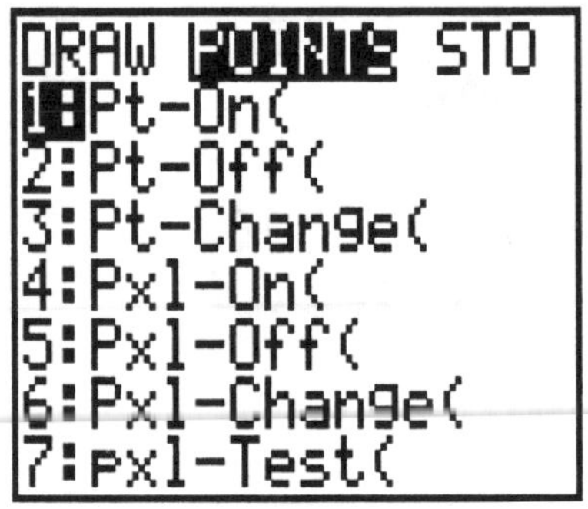

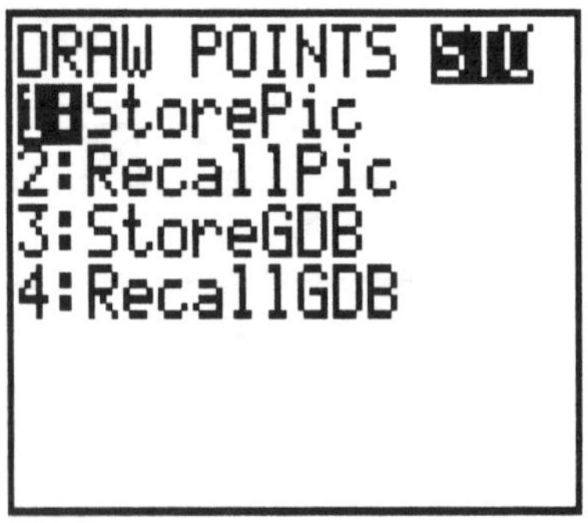

VARS/Y-VARS MENU: These menus are very different for the TI-82 and the TI-81. For the TI-82, choose the submenu that refers to the source of the intended variable.

TI-82 VARS:

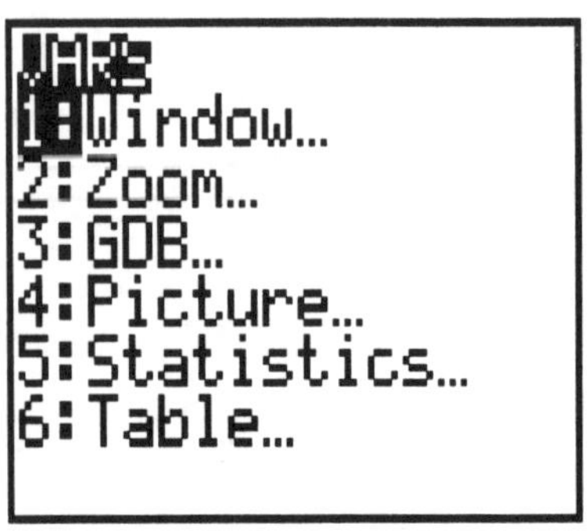

TI-81 VARS: There are 5 submenus in the **VARS** menu. Most of the variables used in statistics, matrices, and graphing can be found in the following menus:

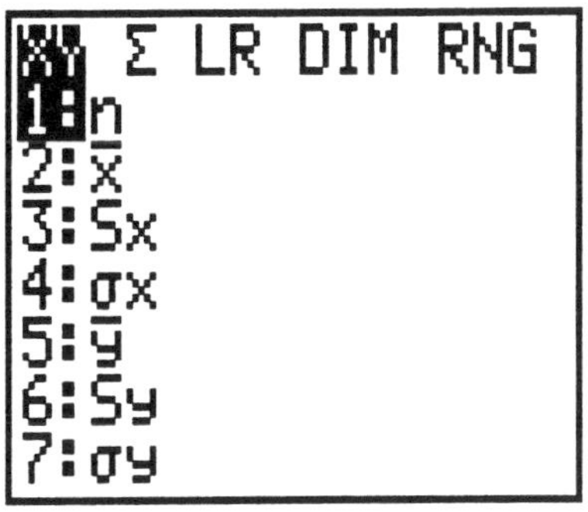

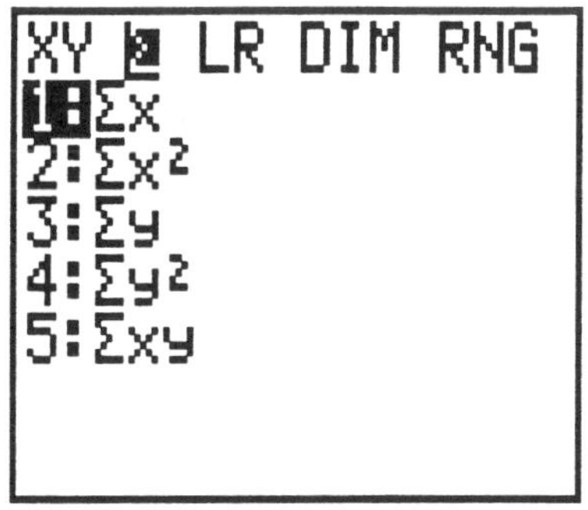

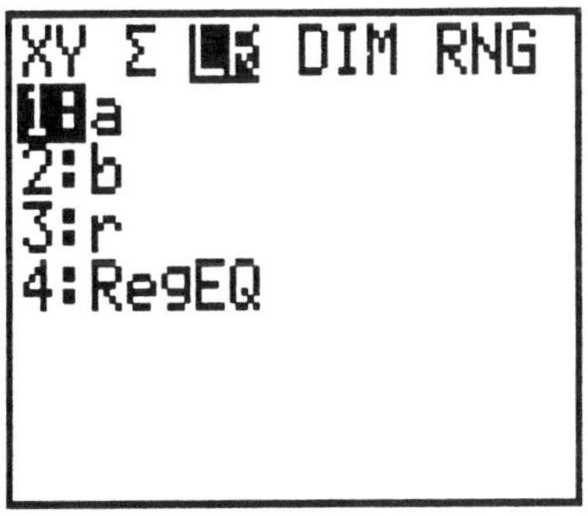

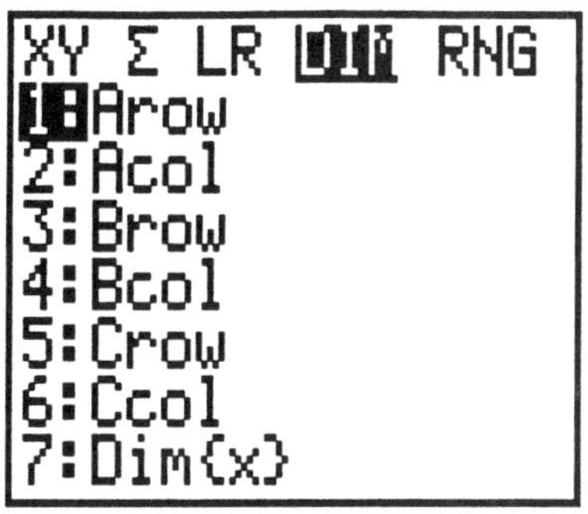

TI-82 Y-VARS:

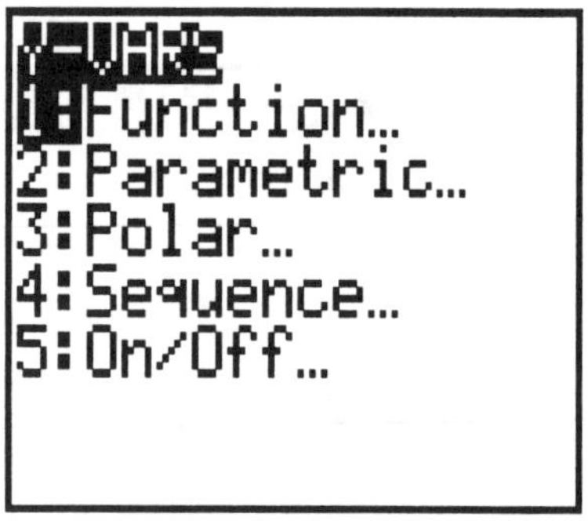

TI-81 Y-VARS: The **Y-VARS** menu contains both the Y variables and the names of the parametric variables. The three menus **Y**, **ON**, and **OFF** all look alike. The first is used to call up function names while the others are used to turn the various function names on or off for graphing.

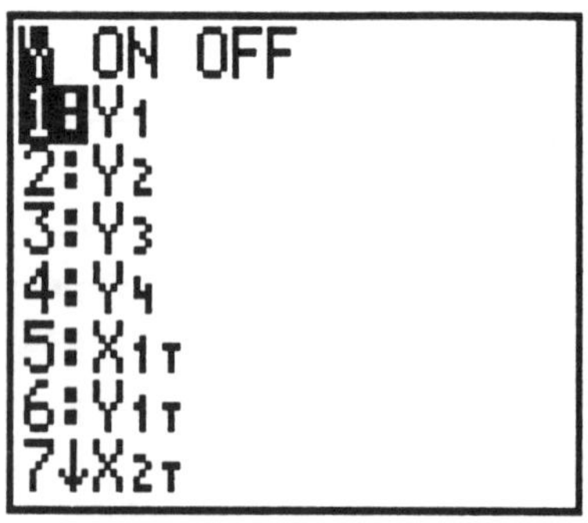

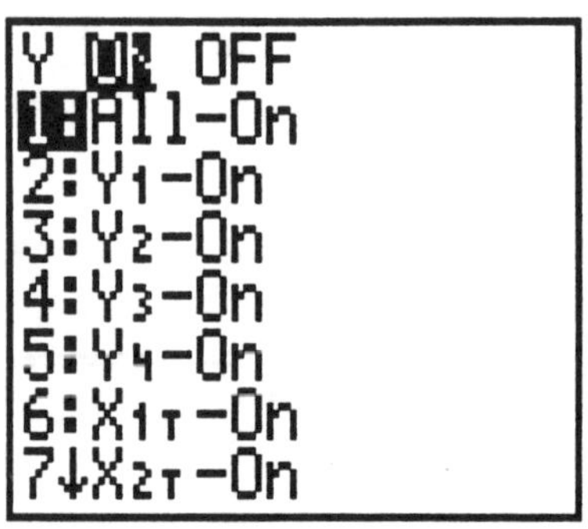

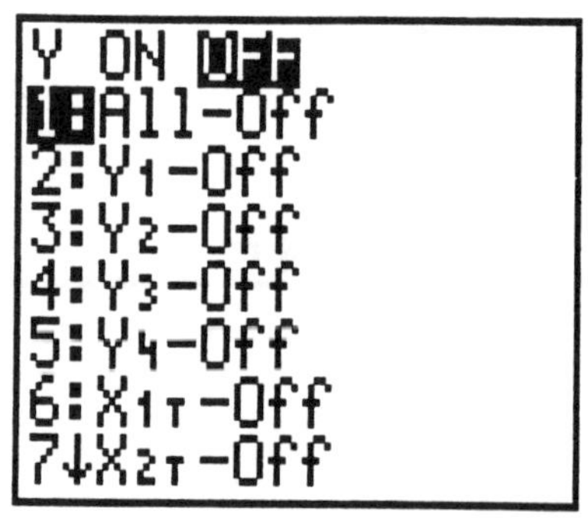

The TI-82 has two other menus that may be useful when programming: [2nd] [MATRX] (ANGLE) and [2nd] [STAT] (LIST). LIST has two submenus, as you can see here:

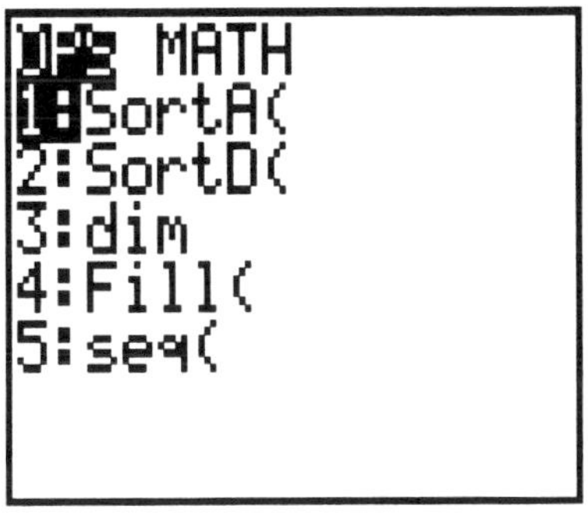

SECTION 9

Answers to Additional Problems

Answers to All Additional Problems

Page 4

1. The data does appear somewhat linear. If a line were used to model the data, the slope would be the change per year in the time to swim 100 meters.

2. The scatter plot shows that the relationship between life expectancy and the year born is nearly linear with a positive slope.

3. The scatter plot here appears somewhat linear, but to be realistic, it cannot continue to be linear. If it were to remain linear, it would eventually dip below two, then below one, and eventually less than zero. While small sections of many graphs may appear linear, there is often good reason why the entire relationship cannot be linear.

Page 12

1. The graphs of $y = c$, $y = |x|$, and $y = x^2$ are even functions.

2. The graphs of $y = x$, $y = x^3$, $y = \frac{1}{x}$, and $y = \sin(x)$ are odd functions.

3. Each of the toolkit functions is listed below with the actual domain and range as well as a suggested viewing window.

Function	Domain	Range	(Xmin, Xmax)	(Ymin, Ymax)
$y = c$	All reals	$y = c$	$(-10, 10)$	$(-10, 10)$
$y = x$	All reals	All reals	$(-5, 5)$	$(-1, 7)$
$y = \|x\|$	All reals	$y \geq 0$	$(-10, 10)$	$(-10, 10)$
$y = x^2$	All reals	$y \geq 0$	$(-5, 5)$	$(-5, 25)$
$y = x^3$	All reals	All reals	$(-5, 5)$	$(-25, 25)$
$y = \frac{1}{x}$	$x \neq 0$	$y \neq 0$	$(-5, 5)$	$(-5, 5)$
$y = \sqrt{x}$	$x \geq 0$	$y \geq 0$	$(0, 25)$	$(0, 5)$
$y = e^x$	All reals	$y > 0$	$(-5, 5)$	$(-2, 16)$
$y = \ln x$	$x > 0$	All reals	$(-2, 16)$	$(-5, 5)$
$y = \sin(x)$	All reals	$-1 \leq y \leq 1$	$(-2\pi, 2\pi)$	$(-2, 2)$

4. To write the function on the TI-81, enter $Y_1 = (X \leq -2)4 + (X > -2)(X < 2)X^2 + (X \geq 2)4$.

Page 14

1. At 8% it only takes 8 years and 9 months for money compounded monthly to double. At 6.5% it takes 10 years and 9 months.

2. The projectile stays in the air the longest when the angle is 16 degrees (to the nearest degree). At this angle the projectile has a range of 93.8 meters. You can use tables of values or graphs of the height and horizontal distance to see that this is the maximum range.

3. a. The function approaches 500 as t gets large.
   b. The function reaches 250 at approximately $t = 13.863$.
   c. From the graph and the table of values, you can see that the greatest change in the values of the function occurs near $t = 13.863$. This is also the point on the graph with the greatest slope.

Page 16

1. It appears that the graphs are shifted horizontally c units: to the left if $c > 0$; to the right if $c < 0$.

2. From these graphs it appears that the function is compressed (if $c > 1$) or stretched ($0 < c < 1$) in the horizontal direction. If $c < 0$ the same is true but the graph is flipped across the y-axis.

3. The parameter c stretches ($c > 1$) or compresses ($0 < c < 1$) the graph in the vertical direction. Again, if $c < 0$ the graph is flipped, but this time across the x-axis.

4. The graph of $g(x)$ looks as if it has been moved 1 unit to the right, stretched by a factor of 3 in the vertical direction, and moved up 2 units.

Page 18

1. One way to think of $f(x)$ as a composition is to write it as $g(h(x))$ where $h(x) = x^2 - 2$ and $g(x) = \frac{1}{x}$. The domain of $h(x)$ is all real numbers, but in the composition an x value of $\pm\sqrt{2}$ will make the denominator zero. The domain of the composition will be all reals not equal to $\pm\sqrt{2}$.

2. Let $f(x) = g(h(x))$, where $h(x) = 9 - x^2$ and $g(x) = \sqrt{x}$. The domain of $h(x)$ is all real numbers, but when $x > 3$ or $x < -3$, the values of $h(x)$ are negative. Since the square root function is not real-valued for negative x, we must restrict the domain accordingly. The domain of $f(x)$ then is $-3 \leq x \leq 3$.

3. Let $f(x) = g(h(x))$, where $h(x) = \sin(x)$ and $g(x) = |\frac{1}{x}|$. The domain of $h(x)$ is all real numbers, but when $x = k\pi$ (k an integer), the sine is zero, so these values of x cannot be used in the composition. The domain of $f(x)$ then, is all real numbers not equal to $k\pi$.

4. Let $h(x) = |x| - 2$ and $g(x) = x^3 - 1$. The domain of $h(x)$ is all reals, and $g(x)$ will accept all of the resulting y-values.

5. The composition $f(g(x)) = 6x + 3$, while the composition $g(f(x)) = 6x - 1$. Based on only this one problem, one might hypothesize that compositions of linear functions are linear (true) and that composition is not a commutative operation (also true).

Page 22

1. If you graph the function for the surface area and the constant function $y = 650$, the graphs intersect at roughly $x = 3.485$ and $x = 7.97$. Therefore, the surface area is less than 650 when $3.485 < x < 7.97$.

2. From the intersecting graphs, it appears that it will take 55.8 months to repay the loan. In reality, it could take 55 months with the 55th payment being larger than \$250, or 56 months with the last payment being smaller than \$250. This last payment, sometimes called a *balloon payment*, is usually larger than the regular payments.

Page 23

1. The zeros are exactly $x = -2, 1, 4$, and the turning points are approximately $(-0.726, 10.392)$ and $(2.734, -10.392)$.

2. The only zero is $x = -0.823$, and there is no turning point.

3. The zeros are approximately $x = 0.38$ and $x = 2.62$. The turning point, here an absolute minimum value, is located at the point $(1.78, -15.827)$.

4. The only zero is $x = -1.32$ and the turning points are $(-0.58, 1.38)$ and $(0.58, 0.62)$.

5. This function has no real zeros, but the three turning points are $(-0.76, 8.62)$, $(0, 9)$, and $(0.76, 8.62)$.

6. The zeros are $x = -1$, $x = -2$, $x = 1$ and the turning points are $(-1.69, -0.397)$, $(-1, 0)$, and $(0.462, -2.83)$.

7. The zeros are $x = -0.7$, $x = -0.17$, $x = 1.09$, $x = 3.79$ and the turning points are $(-0.46, 0.89)$, $(0.548, -3.15)$, and $(2.90, 35.258)$.

8. This function has four zeros, at $x = -4.375$, $x = 0.44$, $x = 1.37$, $x = 4.555$. The turning points are $(-2.89, -156.70)$, $(0.9, 4.21)$, and $(3.48, -54.44)$.

9. The zeros are $x = -2.44$, $x = -1$, $x = 0$, $x = 2.44$, $x = 4$ and the turning points are $(-1.94, 24.23)$, $(-0.51, -6.47)$, $(1.43, 35.32)$ and $(3.41, -49.94)$.

Page 27

1. If the base is a circle with diameter x, the girth will be the circumference, which is πx, and the length L cannot exceed $108 - \pi x$. The formula for volume is $\pi \frac{x^2}{4} L$, or $\pi \frac{x^2}{4}(108 - \pi x)$. The maximum volume for this container is 14,851 in^3 and the box has diameter 22.9 inches.

2. The function for the total length of the three sections of cable is $f(x) = \sqrt{(x-10)^2 + 5^2} + \sqrt{x^2 + 10^2} + \sqrt{(x-20)^2 + 15^2}$. The minimum total length is approximately 37.13 units and occurs when $x = 9.51$.

Page 30

1. We need to solve the equation $0.04e^{0.065t} = 0.50$, or $0.04e^{0.065t} - 0.50 = 0$. This will occur when $x = 38.86$ or roughly near the end of 1996, if the model continues to hold. Using the same model it will take 49.52 years to reach \$1.00. This will be the year 2007.

2. We need to set $150 + 450\cos\left(\frac{\pi x}{6}\right) = 500$ and solve for x. The two values between 0 and 12 are 1.297 and 10.703. This means that from late November through early February the store sells over $500 of ski equipment each day.

Page 33

1. The cosine and the line $y = x$ intersect only once, at the point (0.7391, 0.7391).

2. The graphs of $y = x$ and $y = \frac{1}{3}e^x$ intersect twice. The first point is at (0.6191, 1.8573). This is an **attracting fixed point**, as all points around it are attracted to it. The other point is a **repelling fixed point**, as points are repelled from it. To find the other point you must use the inverse of $y = \frac{1}{3}e^x$, which is $y = \ln(3x)$. When you use the log function, the repelling point becomes an attracting point and Picard's method locates it at (1.5121, 4.5363). We conclude that $x = 0.6191$ and $x = 1.5121$ are solutions.

3. Since both of these functions are even, the points of intersection will be symmetric with respect to the y-axis. To find the one in the first quadrant, use $y = x$ and $y = \sqrt{\cos x}$. The points of intersection are (0.8241, 0.6791) and (−0.8241, 0.6791). We conclude that $x = 0.8241$ and $x = -0.8241$ are solutions.

Page 35

1. The standard viewing window $-10 \le x \le 10$ and $-10 \le y \le 10$ is a good viewing window to show the local behavior. You can also graph the horizontal asymptote $y = 3$ on the same graph. If you zoom out by a factor of 3 ($-30 \le x \le 30$ and $-30 \le y \le 30$) most of the graph looks like the asymptote, but there is an abrupt deviation from this line near $x = 2$.

2. The standard viewing window $-10 \le x \le 10$ and $-10 \le y \le 10$ is a good viewing window to show the local behavior. You can also graph the oblique asymptote $y = x - 3$ along with the graph. If you zoom out by a factor of 3 ($-30 \le x \le 30$ and $-30 \le y \le 30$) most of the graph looks like the asymptote, but there is an abrupt deviation from this line near $x = 2$.

3. Regardless of the viewing window, the graph of this function is going to look like the line $y = x + 2$. The hole in the graph at the point (3, 5) will be very difficult to see on the calculator.

4. If you graph this function using the viewing window $-5 \le x \le 5$ and $-5 \le y \le 15$, you will notice that the graph looks a lot like a parabola, except near $x = 2$. The line $x = 2$ is a vertical asymptote, but the rational function is asymptotic to the parabola $y = x^2 + x - 1$ as you move away from $x = 2$.

5. Since this graph is identical to the graph of $y = \frac{1}{x-4}$, except for a hole at the point $(0,0)$, a good window for viewing the local behavior might be $-2 \le x \le 10$ and $-10 \le y \le 10$. Zooming out by a factor of 3 reveals the global behavior. This function is very close to zero for most x-values, excepting near $x = 4$.

Page 38

1. If the airline only services one city, it just taxis from one end of the runway to the other. Two cities would give the airline 1 route; three cities 3 routes; four cities 6 routes; and so on. The points to fit the curve through are (1,0), (2,1), (3,3), and (4,6). The four cubic functions that equal zero at three of the x-values and equal the y-coordinate at the fourth x-coordinate are $y_1 = 1(x-1)(x-2)(x-3)$, $y_2 = 0(x-2)(x-3)(x-4)$, $y_3 = -\frac{3}{2}(x-1)(x-2)(x-4)$ and $y_4 = \frac{1}{2}(x-1)(x-3)(x-4)$. When these four functions are added togther, the sum is simply $f(x) = \frac{x(x-1)}{2}$.

Page 40

1. $\left(1 + \frac{0.06}{12}\right)^{12} = 1.0617$, so the effective rate is 6.17%.

2. Here $e^{0.08} = 1.0833$, so the effective rate is 8.33%.

3. For small values of n, the two functions are farther apart as x gets larger. For large values of n, the functions are still not equal, but they stay closer much longer. Because of the resolution on the graphing calculator, it is difficult to see this. Try letting $n = 1$ and graphing on the window $30 \le x \le 35$ and $5 \le y \le 7$. Now let $n = 12$ and notice the difference.

Page 42

1. There are any number of ways to solve for x if $50000(1 + .07)^x = 250000$: tracing and zooming; using a table of values; using a numerical method like Bisection; or solving algebraically. The algebraic solution is $\ln(5) \div \ln(1.07) = 23.79$

2. Again, this is simply $1700(1.10)^{18} = 9451.86$. Let's hope they also added some to it on a regular basis. See the section on annuities for a way to compute the amount in an account into which money is added on a regular basis.

Page 44

1. Either by using the formula, $f(x) = \frac{250(1.0075^x - 1)}{0.0075}$, or the recursive formula in the program, the amount would be $48,378.57.

2. The total in the account would be $42,111.06.

3. Start with $750,000 and take out $50,000. With this in the calculator as the last answer, press [2nd] [(−)], multiply by 1.08 and subtract 50000. Now press [ENTER]. This is the first day of the second year. Press [ENTER] 19 more times, and you now have $948,677.58 in the account. You could afford to pay yourself more each year.

4. If your parents put $600 in each year for 18 years, and the account is compounded only once each year, at the end of 18 years, there will be $36,811.36 in the account. This amount is $27,359.50 more than if your parents had only invested the $1700. If the 10% were compounded monthly and they invested $50 each month, the account would yield $39,480.02.

Page 46

1. The scatter plot of the data shows that it is fairly linear, so the least-squares regression line should be an appropriate model.

   a. The least-squares line has equation $y = -0.043x + 2.179$.
   b. The slope tells us that for every degree the incline is raised, the ball takes 0.043 fewer seconds to roll down the incline.
   c. At 24 degrees, the ball should take approximately $-0.043(24) + 2.179$, or about 1.15 seconds.
   d. Let $-0.043x + 2.179 = 1$ and solve. $x = 27.4$ degrees.
   e. Obviously, if the angle is zero, it cannot take 2.179 seconds to roll. In the range we were given, the model is fairly good.

Page 50

1. Possible models follow, where t represents the years since 1981, that is, in 1981, $t = 0$.

$$f(t) = 92.0e^{.037t}$$
$$f(t) = 958.1e^{.076t}$$
$$f(t) = 4,227e^{.088t}$$

The Consumer Price Index is growing at a rate of roughly 3.7% annually. The cost of attending a public college is going up by about 7.6% per year while the cost of attending a private college is growing at a rate of 8.8%, more than double the Consumer Price Index.

2. a. This relationship looks like a power function.
   b. Taking the logs of both coordinates produces a line.
   c. The slope of the line is roughly 0.81, and the intercept is very close to zero.
   d. A function which models this relationship is $f(x) = x^{0.81}$.

Page 55

1. The period is 12 (months) and the amplitude is $\frac{14.65-9.68}{2} = 2.485$. The vertical shift is $14.65 - 2.485 = 12.165$. The graph has also been shifted approximately 3 units to the right. If x represents the the number of the month, (1 = January 21st), the equation is $y = 2.485 \sin\left(\frac{\pi}{6}(x-3)\right) + 12.165$.
2. The equation is $y = 220 \sin(120\pi x)$.
3. The wave quickly approaches a square wave, a wave with period 2π which equals 1 for $2k\pi < x < (2k+1)\pi$ and -1 for $(2k+1)\pi < x(2k+2)\pi$, k and integer.

Page 62

1. Define the following matrices.

$$B = \begin{bmatrix} 1.005 & 0 \\ -1 & 0 \end{bmatrix}$$

$$C = \begin{bmatrix} 500000 & 2500 \end{bmatrix}$$

Start with C. Run the matrix power program raising B to the 480th power. Multiply $C \times A$ and adjust the amount in matrix C until you have a balance of 0. This is approximately \$2,751.07 each month.

2. Define the following matrices.

$$B = \begin{bmatrix} 1.005 & 0 \\ -1.00166 & 1.00166 \end{bmatrix}$$

$$C = \begin{bmatrix} 500000 & 2000 \end{bmatrix}$$

Start with C. Run the matrix power program raising B to the 480th power. Multiply $C \times A$ and adjust the amount in matrix C until you have a balance of 0. You will be able to withdraw approximately \$2,087.62 first month and eventually withdraw \$4,642.99 the last month.

Index

NOTES

NOTES

Graphing Calculator **Lab Manual**

CASIO 7700G™

Contemporary Precalculus
through applications

Graphing Calculator

L A B M A N U A L

CASIO 7700G™

John Goebel

Donita Robinson

Nicole Arendas

Janson Publications, Inc.
Dedham, Massachusetts

Revised Edition

Printed in the United States of America.

9 8 7 6 5 1 2 3 4 5 6 7 8 9

CONTENTS

PREFACE

When the Mathematics Department at the North Carolina School of Science and Mathematics first set out to write a new precalculus course, we found very little existing computer software that would graph functions, fit curves to data points, and work with matrices. In spite of this, we set out to write a course that was applications-oriented, that allowed students to investigate patterns and problems, and that took advantage of the capabilities of the computer. In order to implement the course fully, we wrote our own software so that students could easily use the computer as a tool.

By the time our precalculus course, *Contemporary Precalculus through Applications*, was published, we saw several developments which validated the assumptions made while designing the course. First and foremost was the release of the *NCTM Curriculum Standards for School Mathematics*. In that document NCTM recommends that students solve real-world problems and that they use the computer as a tool, to help both in understanding important concepts and in solving problems. NCTM further recommends that students learn to use functions for developing mathematical models.

Another development that has dramatically changed the mathematics classroom, and, as a result, our course, is the continuing evolution of the graphing calculator as a viable instructional tool. Studies indicate that very few mathematics classrooms have a computer together with an adequate projection device for classroom demonstrations. Currently, for the combined cost of one computer and a projection device, a school can put a calculator into the hands of every student in several classrooms. These calculators are powerful teaching tools. By using them, students can do calculations quickly. This helps them notice patterns. They can graph and visualize the behavior of functions; they can plot data and then find a function to model the data; and they can use matrices to solve real and interesting problems. With these tools in the hands of students, we are approaching the goal of making mathematics more accessible to a broader student population. It is our belief that every student, from the strongest to the weakest, will benefit by having a graphing calculator available during class discussions, when doing homework, and when taking tests.

The purpose of this *Graphing Calculator Lab Manual* is to help students and teachers alike more quickly discover and use the power of the graphing calculator. The goal is not to help students do the old mathematics faster or more accurately, but rather to explore some new and exciting mathematics and to think about and mathematically model the world around them. The numerical and

graphical capabilities of these calculators will force us all to re-examine continually what we teach and how we teach it. The opportunity for students to learn how to use mathematics and for teachers to teach problem solving may finally be here.

We would like to thank the many teachers who have used the programs and problems in this book and especially the students and our colleagues in the Mathematics Department at the North Carolina School of Science and Mathematics for their helpful suggestions. We would also like to thank Joseph Calamoneri and Dennis Reer of Casio, Inc. for their assistance in preparing this manuscript.

INTRODUCTION

This manual assumes that the user has some experience with the Casio *fx*-7700 graphing calculator. The user should work through the Quick-Start Tutorial provided in the *Owner's Manual* to become familiar with the keypad. If further orientation to the calculator is needed, the user should work through Chapter One of the *Owner's Manual* to get better acquainted with the features of the calculator, including the modes and menus.

The Casio *fx*-7700 Modes. Before using the Casio *fx*-7700 for a particular task, the user must set the calculator to the proper mode. Since this is the first step in every process, and a very important one at that, it is worth some explanation here. Setting the correct mode before writing a program is critical, as the program must be written in the appropriate mode for the task the program is designed to perform. For example, a statistics program must be written in statistics mode and a program designed to graph parametric equations must be written in parametric graphing mode. The user should become familiar with the modes, as outlined in the *Owner's Manual*, and should get in the habit of checking the mode before doing any calculations, solving any problems, graphing any functions, and especially before writing any programs. The normal mode settings for most of the explorations and programs in this book are as follows.

Sys mode:	RUN	Press [MODE] [1]
Cal mode:	COMP	Press [MODE] [+]
REG mode:	LIN	Press [MODE] [4]
Stat mode:	STO	Press [MODE] [SHIFT] [1]
Graph type:	REC	Press [MODE] [SHIFT] [+]
Draw type:	CONNECT	Press [MODE] [SHIFT] [5]

At the beginning of each section and each program, we will warn you if the mode should be anything different from those listed above. In addition, we will assume that the calculator is set in radian mode when working with angles and trigonometric functions. To use radian mode, press [SHIFT] [1] (DGR) and press [F2] (**Rad**) [EXE]

The above key sequence is illustrative of the instructions we will give throughout the book. We will try to give you the exact keystrokes for the processes outlined in the text. These keystrokes will be enclosed in boxes. The symbol in the box

will be for the primary function of that key. The symbol following the key strokes (in parentheses) will tell you the actual command the key sequence activates. For example, the above sequence of keystrokes [SHIFT] [1] (DGR) means that you will press the [SHIFT] key followed by the [1] key, but the calculator will respond by displaying the menu to set the calculator to the degree, radian, or gradient mode. Then pressing [F2] (**RAD**) followed by [EXE] will set the calculator to the radian mode.

When writing programs to do many of the tasks that the calculator will not otherwise do, we made the programs fairly straightforward. We realize that the user may want to modify programs to make them more versatile or to provide more prompts. We tried to write programs simple enough so that most users would take the time to enter them and could easily understand how they work. We hope that the user will take these rather basic programs and modify and improve them as necessary for broader application.

SECTION 1

Linear Data

Scatter Plots

Problem Statement

Archeologists can determine the height of ancient humans by simply finding one bone of the body and using the linear relationship that exists between the length of that bone and height. To find such a relationship, data is gathered from modern man. Using the data in the table below, graph a scatter plot and find a linear relationship between the length of the tibia and height.

tibia in cm	29	31	32	34	35	36	37	39	40	41
height in cm	153	157	159	164	167	169	172	176	179	183

GRAPHING CALCULATOR SOLUTION. To determine if the relationship is linear, we would like to draw a scatter plot on the calculator. To enter the data into the Casio fx-7700 graphing calculator, follow the procedure below:

- Be sure that the calculator is in Run Mode and in Rectangular Coordinate Mode. Press [MODE] [1] and [MODE] [SHIFT] [+].
- Set the calculator to the Statistics Draw Mode. Press [MODE] [SHIFT] [3].
- Since we may want to use the data later, press [MODE] [SHIFT] [1] (Data Store Mode).
- Get the Statistics Menu, press [MODE] [÷].
- Notice the options at the bottom of the screen. These operations are performed by pressing the function keys [F1] through [F6] across the top row of keys.

- Begin by clearing data already in memory. Select the **EDIT** operation by pressing [F2]. Now press [F3] (**ERASE**) followed by [F1] (**YES**) to erase all data.

- As you enter data into the Casio, it is plotted on a scatter plot. Be sure to set the range first to accomodate the data. Press [Range] and enter the values for Xmin, max, and scl and Ymin, max, and scl. After entering the Yscl and pressing [EXE] you will see the settings for parametric functions. Simply press [EXE] three additional times to exit the range menu. Also be sure to clear the screen (press [SHIFT] [F5] and [EXE]).

- To enter data, enter the first coordinate, [SHIFT] [→] (the comma), the second coordinate and [F1] (the **DT** option). Notice the data point on the scatter plot.

- To enter the second data point, simply enter the next ordered pair. After the last ordered pair, you may view the data and edit any incorrect entries. Use the arrow keys to move around the data set. To see the scatter plot after editing data, you need to press the [F6] (**CAL**) key. (You may need to press [MODE] [4] to get the correct menu.) The only way to call back a scatter plot, even if the data were all correct, is to go change one piece of data, then change it back. Again, press [F6] (**CAL**) to see the scatter plot.

Below is the scatter plot for the above tibia/height data, using a viewing window of $25 \le x \le 45$ and $150 \le y \le 200$.

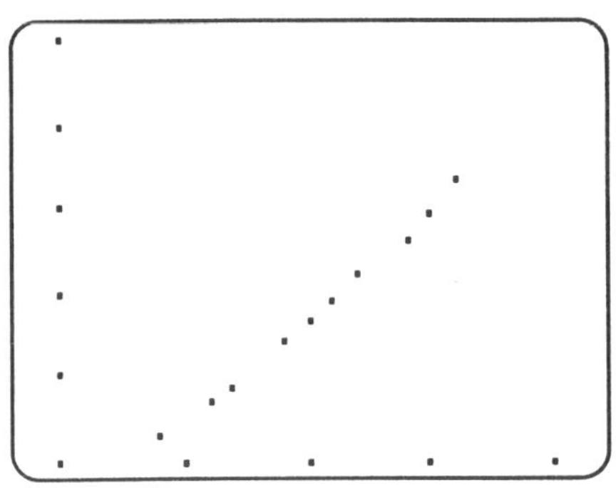

Many keystrokes are required in the above process just to graph a scatter plot. The program below will accomplish the same results with fewer strokes to remember and key in. See Section 8 for instructions on entering a program. **Note:** The calculator mode in which you enter a program becomes part of the program, so you must be in the proper mode before entering and storing each program.

Note. The last section of this book gives some programming hints, but throughout the book it is assumed that the user is familiar with the keys and menus of the

Casio *fx*-7700. You may need to refer to your *Power Graphic fx-7700 Owner's Manual.*

Programming Solution. To cut down on the number of key strokes, you may want to write a short program to enter data and plot the scatter plot. Before entering this program be sure the calculator is still in linear regression mode and data store mode.

Program Code: SCATTER

Program Code	Comments
'SCATTER'	
Cls	Clear the graphing screen.
Scl	Clear the statistics memory.
"MIN X"? →E	Input minimum x-value for viewing window.
"MAX X"? →F	Input maximum x-value for viewing window.
"MIN Y"? →C	Input minimum y-value for viewing window.
"MAX Y"? →D	Input maximum y-value for viewing window.
Range E,F,0,C,D,0	Setting range or viewing window.
"NO. POINTS"? →A	Input number of data points.
Defm 90	Assigning sufficient memory for up to 20 data points.
21 →B	Begin subscript for array to store data points.
Lbl 1	Begin the loop to enter data.
"ENTER X"? →E[B]	Enter and store first coordinate of points.
"ENTER Y"? →E[B+A]	Enter and store second coordinates.
E[B],E[B+A] DT	Storing data in Regression Mode (To input *DT*, you may need to press [MODE] [÷] to recall the Data Input Menu. Press [EXE] to resume editing the program.)
B+1 →B	Incrementing the counter.
B < A + 21 ⇒Goto 1	End of loop to enter data.
"Press G-T"	Press G ↔ T to see graph.

Additional Problems

1. The times (in seconds) for the 100 meters backstroke for women at the Olympics are given in the following table. Does the relationship seem to be

linear? If a line were used to model this data, how would the slope of the line be interpreted?

Date	Time	Date	Time	Date	Time
1924	83.20	1952	74.30	1972	65.80
1928	82.00	1956	72.90	1976	61.83
1932	79.40	1960	69.30	1980	60.86
1936	78.90	1964	67.70	1984	62.55
1948	74.40	1968	66.20	1988	60.89

2. The life expectancy of males born between 1920 and 1988 are given in the following table. What type of relationship exists between the life expectancy and the year of birth?

Date	1920	1930	1940	1950
Years	53.6	58.1	60.8	65.6
Date	1960	1970	1980	1988
Years	66.6	67.1	70.0	71.5

Source: U.S. Dept. of Health and Human Services,

National Center for Health Statistics

3. The size of families in the United States has been decreasing in recent years. The following table gives the average size of U. S. households from 1940 to 1990. Make a scatter plot and describe the relationship.

Date	1940	1950	1955	1960	1965
Size	3.67	3.37	3.33	3.33	3.29
Date	1970	1975	1980	1985	1990
Size	3.14	2.94	2.76	2.69	2.63

Source: U.S. Bureau of the Census

Linear Data and the Median-Median Line

If the ordered pairs of data appear linear, you can fit a line to the data. Two common lines used to model linear data are the median-median line and the least squares regression line. Both give a relationship between the length of the tibia and height. The median-median line can be computed by hand fairly easily and has the advantage that it is resistant to data points that appear to be out of line with the rest of the data set. The regression line, or least squares line, while more widely used, is more difficult to find. The calculator will find the slope and intercept of this line for you. (See Section 5: "Linear Data and the Least Squares Line".)

Problem Statement

A basketball is dropped from different heights and the height of the bounce is measured. Find the relationship between the height of the drop and the height of the bounce.

MEDIAN-MEDIAN LINE SOLUTION. The scatter plot for this data reveals that there appears to be a linear relationship. One of the linear equations that can be used to model this relationship is the median-median line. To find the equation of this line, divide the data set into three fairly equal groups. Since the medians of subgroups of the data are to be used, the data should be put in increasing order. To do this, order the first coordinates. Be sure to keep the ordered pairs together as they are divided into three groups. Once the first coordinates of each group are in order, find the median for these coordinates. Next find the median for the second coordinates of the first subgroup of data. The point described by the ordered pair formed from the medians of the first and second coordinates is the lower summary point. The height and bounce data below serves as an example:

height (in)	41	43	45	47	49	51	53	55	57	59
bounce (in)	27	28	29	30	32	33	34	35	36	37

The median height for the lower group is 43 and the median bounce is 28. For the second group, the median height is 50 and the median bounce is 32.5. For the upper group, the median height is 57 while the median bounce is 36. These are the summary points. The slope of the median-median line will be the slope of the line connecting the lower and upper summary points. In this example, the slope is

$$(36 - 28)/(57 - 43) = 0.57142857\ldots.$$

The line joining these points will probably not pass through the middle summary point, but this summary point will influence the line. The line must be shifted one-third of the way to the middle summary point, while keeping the slope equal to the slope of the line through the two outer summary points. This could all be done by hand, and part of this process is actually easier to do by hand. Finding the summary points of the three subgroups is easy to do by hand. Programming the Casio fx-7700 to find the summary points is possible, but probably not worth the effort. Given the summary points, the following program will compute the slope, find the vertical distance between the middle summary point and the line, and shift the line one-third of the way toward the summary point. The program will then display the slope and the y-intercept of the line and plot the line over the scatter plot of the set of data.

PROGRAMMING SOLUTION. Run the Median Line Program immediately after running the Scatter Program. Then the data are stored both in Casio's statistical

Program Code: MEDIAN LINE

Program Code	Comments
'MEDIAN'	
Cls	
"INPUT LOWER SUMMARY PT"	
"X = " ? →P	Enter median of x-coordinates of lower subset.
"Y − " ? →Q	Enter median of y-coordinates of lower subset
"INPUT MIDDLE SUMMARY PT"	
"X = " ? →R	Enter median of x-coordinates of middle subset.
"Y = " ? →S	Enter median of y-coordinates of middle subset
"INPUT UPPER SUMMARY PT"	
"X = " ? →T	Enter median of x-coordinates of upper subset.
"Y = " ? →U	Enter median of y-coordinates of upper subset.
(U−Q)÷(T−P)→M	Compute slope.
-PM+Q →Q	Determine y-intercept of first line.
R →X	Store x-coordinate of middle summary point in X.
f_3 →W	Compute y-coordinate on the line for C.
(S−W)÷3+Q →Q	Slide line one-third of the way toward to the middle summary point.
"SLOPE"	
M ◢	Display the slope.
"INTERCEPT"	
Q ◢	Display the y-intercept.
21 →B	Begin loop to draw the scatter plot.
Lbl 1	
Plot E[A],E[A+B]	Plot points.
B+1 →B	
B < A+21 ⇒Goto 1	
Graph Y=f_3	Graph median-median line.

memory and also as an array E[n]. Since you cannot manipulate Casio's statistical variables, it is necessary to save them in a list so that you can access them. After you have found the three summary points, run the following program to find the median-median line and graph it with the scatter plot of the data set. Be sure to set the calculator to regression mode ([MODE] [÷]), linear regression mode ([MODE] [4]), store data mode ([MODE] [SHIFT] [1]) and draw stat graph mode ([MODE] [SHIFT] [3]).

Before running the median line program, be sure to set the range to accommodate your data. Also be sure to store $MX + Q$ as function f_3. Initially this will be the line through the two outer summary points, but in the end it will be the median-median line.

When running the program, you will first see the slope and the "– disp –" prompt. Press [EXE] to see the intercept and [EXE] again to see the scatter plot and median-median line.

Linear Models and a Residual Program

The best way to determine how well a linear model – either the median-median line or a regression line – fits a set of data is to look at the residuals. You can do this with the Casio fx-7700 by writing a program. To use the calculator to look at the residuals, implement the following **RESIDUAL** program, provided you have run the **SCATTER** program to enter the data and entered a linear model as function f_3.

With a data set entered and a linear model stored as function f_3, you can now run this program. It will automatically find the residuals, graph them, and show the value of the largest and smallest residual. Upon running the program, you will first see the graph of the residuals. Press [EXE] to see the values of the smallest and largest residual. Press the [G↔T] key to toggle between the residual plot and the residual range.

If the data is linear, or nearly linear, the residuals should be randomly scattered about the linear model. If this is not the case, you probably should not try to model the data with a linear function.

The graph on the left shows the residuals for the tibia and height data set, using the median-median line. The screen on the right shows the minimum and maximum residuals. Since there is no pattern to the residuals, and they are relatively small in comparison to the original data, the linear model used is an acceptable one to use for the given data set.

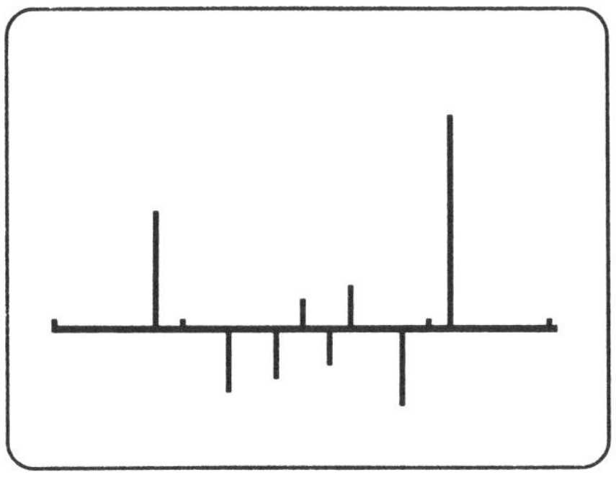

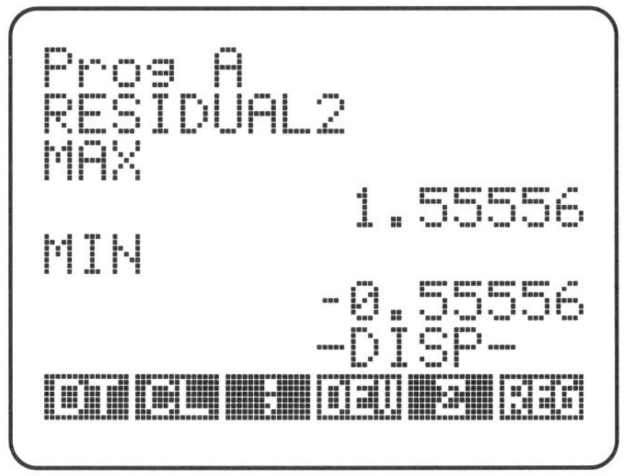

Remember, programs must be written in the mode under which they will run. Set the mode for this program to the linear regression mode, [MODE] [÷] [MODE] [4]; data-store mode, [MODE] [SHIFT] [1]; and statistics draw mode, [MODE] [SHIFT] [3].

Program Code: RESIDUAL

Program Code	**Comments**
'RESIDUAL'	
"INPUT MIN X" ? →E	Input minimum x-coordinate.
"INPUT MAX X" ? →F	Input maximum x-coordinate.
0 →G	This section sets the
0 →H	range for the
21 →B	residuals.
Lbl 5	
E[B] →X	
E[B+A] − f_3 →E[B+2A]	
E[B+2A] > G ⇒E[B+2A] →G	
E[B+2A] < H ⇒E[B+2A] →H	
B+1 →B	
B < A + 21 ⇒Goto 5	
.1(F−E) →Q	
Range E−Q,F+Q,Q,1.5H,1.5G,.3(G−H)	Set the domain and range.
Cls	
21 →B	This section plots the
Lbl 3	residuals.
Plot E[B],E[B+2A]	
Plot E[B],0	
Line	
B+1 →B	
B < A + 21 ⇒Goto 3	
"MAX RESIDUAL"	
G ◢	
"MIN RESIDUAL"	
H ◢	
"PRESS G-T"	

SECTION 2

Functions

Toolkit of Elementary Functions

Problem Statement

Determine the characteristics of the elementary functions. Notice the local behavior (near the origin), the global behavior (the big picture), and the overall behavior of each function.

First set the computer in **RUN** Mode, press [MODE] [1]; **COMP** Calculation Mode, press [MODE] [+]; **REC** Rectangular Graph Type, press [MODE] [SHIFT] [+]; and **CONNECT** Draw Type, press [MODE] [SHIFT] [5].

Enter each of the following functions and graph the non-trigonometric functions using a domain and range which both vary from -10 to 10. This will be referred to as the **Standard** viewing window. Use $-2\pi \le x \le 2\pi$, $-3 \le y \le 3$ as the **Trig** viewing window for the trigonometric functions. Be sure to set the domain and range before graphing the functions.

ELEMENTARY FUNCTIONS. The toolkit of elementary functions includes: $y = c$, $y = x$, $y = |x|$, $y = x^2$, $y = x^3$, $y = \frac{1}{x}$, $y = \sqrt{x}$, $y = e^x$, $y = \ln x$, and $y = \sin x$.

- To enter the functions, enter the function as an expression on a new line of the text window. Next press [SHIFT] [0] ([F]MEM), [F1] (**STO**), followed by a number from 1 to 6. The Casio fx-7700 can store up to 6 functions as f_1 through f_6.
- Enter one function at a time and graph the function using the **Standard** viewing window. Use the **Trig** window for the sine function. To graph a function, press [Graph] [SHIFT] [0] [F2] (**RCL**) followed by the number of the function, from 1 to 6.

- To zoom, press the [F2] (**Zoom**) key and set the zoom factors to 2 by pressing [F2] (**FCT**) again and entering 2 for each factor. To zoom in, press [F3] (**xf**) and to zoom out press [F4] (**x1/f**). If you want to zoom in on a certain point, first press [F1] (**Trace**) and use the arrow keys to move the blinking cursor to a point on the graph. This point will be the center of the new viewing window. Use the zoom-in process to zoom in close to the origin.
- Now press the [Zoom] key again. Use the zoom-out process to zoom out far from the origin to see the global behavior.

Many of the functions used by mathematicians and scientists are simply variations of the function list above. A thorough understanding of these functions is important.

PIECEWISE DEFINED FUNCTIONS. The Casio fx-7700G allows you to combine function definitions using range statements to graph piecewise functions. Suppose you want to graph the function which is defined as follows:

$$f(x) = \begin{cases} 4 & \text{if } x < -1 \\ (x-1)^2 & \text{if } x \geq -1 \end{cases}$$

- Enter 4,[-5,-1] and press [SHIFT], [0] ([F]MEM), [F1] (**STO**) [1] to store this piece of the function as f_1.
- Enter [-1,5],$(X-1)^2$ and press [SHIFT] [0] ([F]MEM), [F1] (**STO**) [2] to store this piece of the function as f_2.
- Set the range to $-5 \leq x \leq 5$ and $-3 \leq y \leq 15$.
- Press [Graph] [SHIFT] [0] ([F]MEM), [F2] (**RCL**) [1] [SHIFT] [EXE] followed by [Graph] [SHIFT] [0] ([F]MEM), [F2] (**RCL**) [2]. Now press [EXE] to see the function. **Note.** You can not use the f_n form of recall for piecewise functions.

Additional Problems

Answer each of the following for the above toolkit functions.

1. Which functions are symmetric with respect to the y-axis? Try graphing $f(x)$ and $f(-x)$. If the two are the same, the graphs are symmetric with respect to the y-axis. These functions are called *even functions*.

2. Which functions are symmetric with respect to the origin? Graph $f(-x)$ and $-f(x)$. If these are indistinguishable, the function is symmetric with respect to the origin. Such functions are called *odd functions.*

3. Note the domain and range of each function. The calculator will graph a function over a large window by simply ignoring any undefined values. Evaluate the functions yourself for positive values, negative values, and zero, to determine the domain and range.

4. Graph the piecewise function

$$f(x) = \begin{cases} 4 & \text{if } x < -2 \\ x^2 & \text{if } x \geq -2 \text{ and } x \leq 2 \\ 4 & \text{if } x > 2 \end{cases}$$

Table of Values of a Function

Problem Statement

If money is invested in the bank at 6.5%, compounded monthly, how long (to the nearest month) will it take for the money to double?

GRAPHING CALCULATOR SOLUTION. One technique for answering any question about a function is to write the function, graph it, and use the [F1] (**Trace**) key to move the cursor along the curve. Another way to look at a function is to look at a table of values. The formula for compounding interest is

$$f(x) = A_0\left(1 + \frac{r}{n}\right)^x$$

where A_0 is the initial amount invested, r is the annual interest rate, n the number of compounding periods per year, and x is the number of months the amount is invested.

To view a single value of the function, first store the function in f_1, using specific values for A_0, r, and n. Now store an x-value in X by pressing [2] [→] [X,θ,T] [EXE]. To see the value of the function for the x you just stored, you must press [SHIFT] and [0] ([F] MEM) followed by either [F2] (**RCL**) or [F3] ($\mathbf{f}_n$) then by pressing the number of the function you want to evaluate. The **RCL** key will recall the expression for the function while $\mathbf{f}_n$ displays the function name. Both will evaluate the desired function for the value stored in X.

PROGRAMMING SOLUTION. The above procedure is very tedious if you want to see several values, but the following program will greatly shorten the process and

display six values of the function. It would be easy to modify the program to see as many values as you like, but each coordinate will take one line on the display. Only three sets of coordinates fit on one screen. When you run the program enter a starting x-value and a step size (either positive or negative). The program will compute the y-coordinate for the initial x-value and the next five values.

Program Code: TABLE

Program Code	Comments
'Graphic'	
"INPUT INITIAL X"? →X	Enter initial value.
"INPUT STEP SIZE"? →S	Enter step size.
0 →I	Initialize counter.
Lbl 1	Begin loop to compute 7 values.
"X="	
X ◢	Display x-coordinate.
"Y="	
f_1 ◢	Display y-coordinate.
S+X →X	Increment X by S.
I+1 →I	Increment counter.
I ≤ 6 ⇒Goto 1	Condition to end loop.

Now run the program and at the first prompt, enter the initial value for x. At the second prompt, enter the step size.

Additional Problems

Use graphs or a table of values to find the following:

1. If the account above paid 8% annually instead of 6.5%, how soon would the amount double?

2. When an object with mass 1 unit is shot into the air at angle θ with some air resistance, (proportional to the velocity), the height at any given time can be given by the function

$$h(t) = (9.8 + V_0 \sin\theta)(1 - e^{-t}) - 9.8t.$$

   a. To find the range of the projectile, we need to know when it hits the ground. Assume that $V_0 = 100$. Find the value of $t, t > 0$, for which $h(t)$ equals zero. Vary the value of θ from 10 to 20 degress and record your answers. When does the projectile stay up the longest?

b. The horizontal component for the projectile is

$$x(t) = V_0 \cos\theta(1 - e^{-t}).$$

For each value of θ above, find the range for the value of t found above to make the height zero. What angle results in the greatest range?

3. When population growth is unconstrained, the population model is exponential. When the growth is constrained, the function is called logistic. For the logistic function

$$f(t) = \frac{500}{1 + 4e^{-0.1t}}$$

use a table of values to evaluate the function for $-30 < t < 30$.

a. What value does the function approach as t gets large?

b. At what point on the graph does the y-value reach half way to the maximum value?

c. When is the population growing at the fastest rate?

Transformations of Functions

Problem Statement

Determine how the following transformations change the graph of the function $f(x)$.

$$f(x) + c; \quad f(x + c); \quad cf(x); \quad f(cx).$$

Graphing Calculator Solution. Enter the simple function $f(x) = x^2$ as f_1 and $f_2 = x^2 + 2$.

- To store the functions, enter the function definition then press [SHIFT] [0] [F1] followed by the number of the function.
- Notice that the calculator can handle up to six functions. As soon as you store one function, press [AC] to clear the screen and enter additional functions the same way.
- Before graphing you must determine the viewing window. Press [Range].
  — Now enter the values for Xmin, max, scl, Ymin, max, scl. For the range variables you may choose the following:

Xmin: -3
max: 3
scl: 1 (Note, each tick mark on the x-axis will equal 1 unit.)
Ymin: -1
max: 9
scl: 1 (Note, each tick mark on the y-axis will equal 1 unit.)

— Leave the values for T and θ alone by pressing [EXE] three times.

- Now the calculator is ready to graph the functions. Press [Graph] [SHIFT] [0] [F2] (**RCL**) followed by the function number and [EXE].

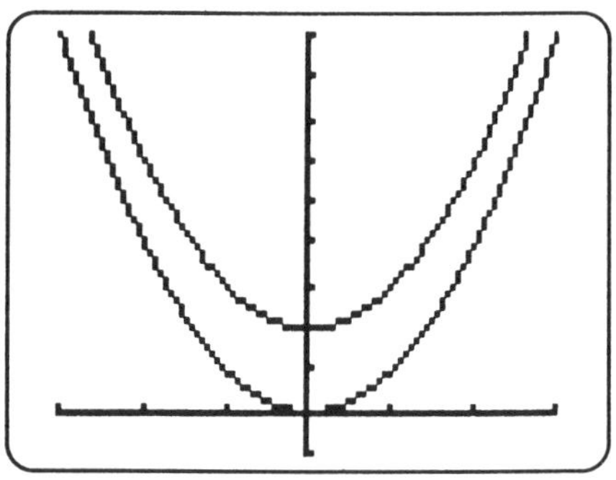

- To graph several functions on the same viewing window, press [Graph] again. The menu to recall additional functions will be displayed. Simply press [F2] and the number of an additional function.
- Another way to graph more than one function is to separate the graphing statements by colons. The colon is entered by accessing the **PRGM** menu - [SHIFT] [Range] - and pressing [F6].

Additional Problems

Determine how altering the equation of a toolkit function "transforms" the graph of the function.

1. Make a generalization of how the graph of $f(x + c)$ differs from the graph of $f(x)$, where c is a constant.

Graph each pair of functions on the same set of axes.

a. $f(x) = x^3$ $g(x) = (x+2)^3$

b. $f(x) = \frac{1}{x}$ $g(x) = \frac{1}{x-1}$

c. $f(x) = \sqrt{x}$ $g(x) = \sqrt{x+3}$

2. Make a generalization of how the graph of $f(cx)$ differs from the graph of $f(x)$, where c is a constant.

Graph each trio of functions on the same set of axes.

a. $f(x) = |x|$ $g(x) = |2x|$ $h(x) = |\frac{1}{2}x|$

b. $f(x) = \sin(x)$ $g(x) = \sin(3x)$ $h(x) = \sin(\frac{1}{3}x)$

c. $f(x) = \sqrt{x}$ $g(x) = \sqrt{4x}$ $h(x) = \sqrt{\frac{x}{4}}$

d. $f(x) = e^x$ $g(x) = e^{-2x}$ $h(x) = e^{-\frac{1}{2}x}$

3. Make a generalization of how the graph of $cf(x)$ differs from the graph of $f(x)$, where c is a constant.

Graph each trio of functions on the same set of axes.

a. $f(x) = x$ $g(x) = 2x$ $h(x) = 0.5x$

b. $f(x) = x^2$ $g(x) = 4x^2$ $h(x) = \frac{1}{4}x^2$

c. $f(x) = \sin(x)$ $g(x) = 3\sin(x)$ $h(x) = \frac{1}{3}\sin(x)$

4. How does the graph of $g(x) = 3|x-1|+2$ compare to the graph of $f(x) = |x|$?

Composition of Functions

Problem Statement

Explain how the function $f(x) = |x^2 - x - 2|$ can be seen as the composition of two functions. Use decomposition of functions to graph $f(x)$.

Graphing Calculator Solution. Let $f(x) = g(x) \circ h(x) = g(h(x))$, where $h(x) = x^2 - x - 2$ and $g(x) = |x|$. Enter into the calculator $h(x)$ as function f_1 and $|f_1|$ as f_2.

- Enter $x^2 - x - 2$ and store as f_1 by pressing the [SHIFT] [0] [F1] [1] keys. To store $|x^2 - x - 2|$ as f_2, press [AC] to clear the screen, then find the absolute value function by pressing [SHIFT] [Graph] (**MATH** menu) and [F3] (**NUM**, the numerical functions). Open the left parenthesis and the recall function 1 by pressing the [SHIFT] [0] [F2] [1] keys. The function name f_n will not work here; you must use the **RCL** option.

- Set the viewing window so that $-10 \leq x \leq 10$ and $-10 \leq y \leq 10$.
- First graph f_1 and then the compostion f_2, which is $g(h(x))$. When are the graphs of $h(x)$ and $g(h(x))$ the same? When are they different?

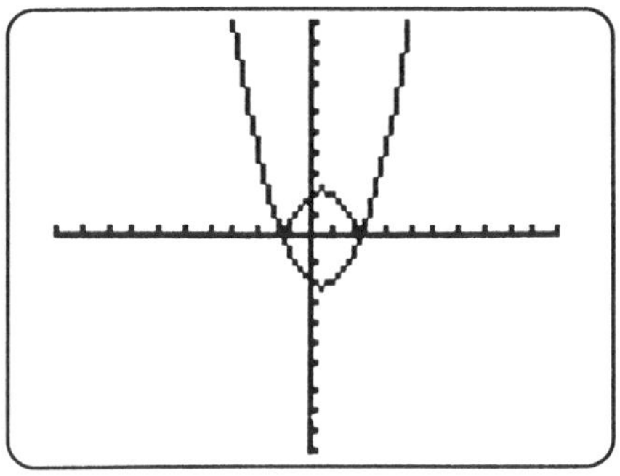

Additional Problems

Explain how the following functions can be written as a composition of functions. Use decomposition to explain the graph of each function. How does the domain of $f(x)$ compare to the domains of the component functions?

1. $f(x) = \dfrac{1}{x^2 - 2}$
2. $f(x) = \sqrt{9 - x^2}$
3. $f(x) = |\dfrac{1}{\sin(x)}|.$
4. $f(x) = (|x| - 2)^3 - 1$
5. The composition of two linear functions is itself a linear function. Given $f(x) = 2x - 1$ and $g(x) = 3x + 2$, graph $f(g(x))$ and $g(f(x))$. What other conclusion about the composition of functions is suggested by these graphs?

Inverse Functions and Relations

Problem Statement

The population since 1790 in North Carolina can be approximated by the exponential equation $p = 383467e^{0.0148(t-1790)}$. Such an approximation or model roughly fits the data for past years and can be used to predict the approximate

population for years in the near future. Suppose you would like to know in what year the population will reach 10 million or any other level.

GRAPHING CALCULATOR SOLUTION. Perhaps the simplest way to answer any question about this function is to trace along the graph until the coordinates of the point are close to either the year or the population level of interest. Another solution involves solving the equation for the year (t), given any desired population level. If it is possible to solve uniquely for the original independent variable, you could form the inverse function and simply substititute in the population and find the year. The inverse function for the population would be

$$t = 1790 + \frac{\ln p - \ln 383467}{0.0148}.$$

To graph this function, the domain and range (of $p(t)$) need to be interchanged.

- Store the inverse function $f_2 = 1790 + (\ln X - \ln 383467)/0.0148$.
- Store 10,000,000 in X (10000000 [→] [X, θ, T]) [EXE]. Press [SHIFT] [0] ([F]MEM) [F2] (**RCL**) [2] [EXE] to see the year in which the model predicts that the population will reach 10,000,000.

GRAPHS OF A FUNCTION AND ITS INVERSE FUNCTION. If a function has an inverse relation that is also a function, both can be stored as functions (as function definitions). In order to graph the function and its inverse on the same graph, the viewing window must be restricted to the same interval for both the x- and y-coordinates. The graph of both functions reveals several interesting facts about functions and inverses.

- Graph $y = 2x - 3$ and its inverse, $y = \dfrac{x+3}{2}$, on the window $x \in [-10, 10]$, $y \in [-10, 10]$.
  - — Zoom in on the point of intersection. Note the coordinates of this point.
  - — Enter the function $y = x$ as f_3. What do you notice?
- Graph $y = e^x$ and $y = \ln x$ on the window $x \in [-3, 3]$ and $y \in [-3, 3]$.
- Graph $y = x^3$ and $y = \sqrt[3]{x}$ on the window $x \in [-10, 10]$ and $y \in [-10, 10]$. Zoom in by setting both of the zoom factors to 3. Press [Zoom], select **F2** (**FCT**) and enter 3 for both the Xfct and the Yfct. Press [EXE] to store these factors. Press [F2] again and select **F3** (xf). If you have entered the functions separated by colons, you will first see the original graph and then the composition. Each time you press the [SHIFT] [F2] [F3] sequence, the calculator will zoom in by the a factor of 3 in each direction.

GRAPHS OF A FUNCTION AND ITS INVERSE RELATION. If you cannot uniquely solve for the independent variable of a function in terms of the dependent variable, the function is not one-to-one. That is, there is more than one y for some of the x's, and hence there is no inverse function. By plotting individual points you can still see the original function and its inverse relation. The following program will plot points on the function and its inverse relation.

Be sure to put the calculator in the **REC/PLT** mode. Press [MODE] [SHIFT] [+] and [MODE] [SHIFT] [6].

Program Code: INVERSE RELATION GRAPHS

Program Code	Comments
'INVERSE'	
Cls	Clear the graphing window.
"INPUT MIN X"? →A	
"INPUT MAX X"? →B	
(B−A)÷12 →S	
Range A,B,S,.67A,.67B,S	Setting the Range.
(B−A)÷96 →D	Defining the x-increment.
A →U	
Lbl 1	Begin loop to plot points.
U →X	
f_1 →Y	
Plot U,Y	Plotting points of the function.
Plot Y,U	Plotting points of the inverse.
U+D →U	Incrementing U.
U < B ⇒Goto 1	

- After the program is entered, press [MODE] [1] to store the program and return to Run Mode.
- Be sure you have entered into function f_1 the original function. Try $y = x^2$.
- The program can now be run.
- In order to run the program, press the [SHIFT] [Range] [F3], the program number, and [EXE]. Enter -10 for MIN X value and +10 for MAX X value.
- Press [G↔T]

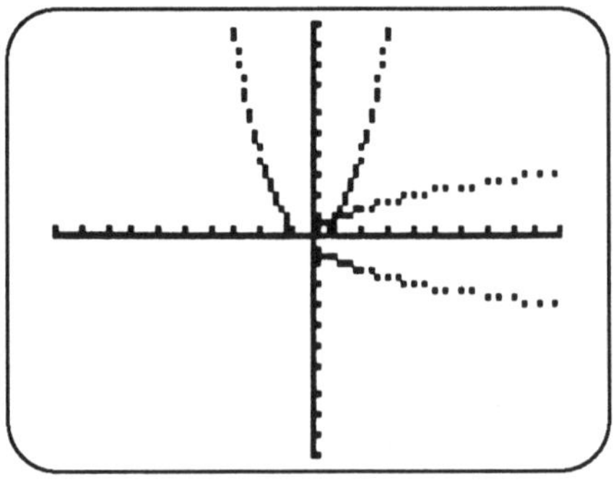

Solving Inequalities

Problem Statement

The average temperature in Durham can be modeled by the trigonometric functions $f(x) = 60 - 21\cos\left(\frac{\pi x}{6}\right)$, where x is the month number from 1 through 12. A certain crop will only grow when the average temperature is greater than 45 degrees. Of course, the assumption is that when the temperature averages 45 degrees Fahrenheit, it does not dip below freezing.

Graphing Calculator Solution. We want to know when the function $f(x) = 60 - 21\cos\left(\frac{\pi x}{6}\right)$ is greater than 45. We could graph $f(x)$ and $g(x) = 45$ and find where $f(x) > g(x)$. We can then shade the desired region and by finding the points of intersection, determine the desired interval. Be sure you have specified radians as the unit of angular measurement, press [SHIFT] [1] [F2] (**Rad**) [EXE].

- Enter $60 - 21\cos\left(\frac{\pi x}{6}\right)$ and store this as function f_1 and 45 as f_2.
- Set the range so that $0 \leq x \leq 12$ and $35 \leq y \leq 85$.
- Be sure you are in **INEQ** mode, press [MODE] [SHIFT] [÷]. Now when you press [Graph] and [F2] the **Graph Y**< prompt will be displayed. Recall function f_1. Press [SHIFT] [EXE] and then press [Graph] [F1] (**Graph Y** >) and recall function f_2. The calculator will shade the region above f_2 but still below f_1.

- Use the trace feature to find the endpoints of the desired interval.

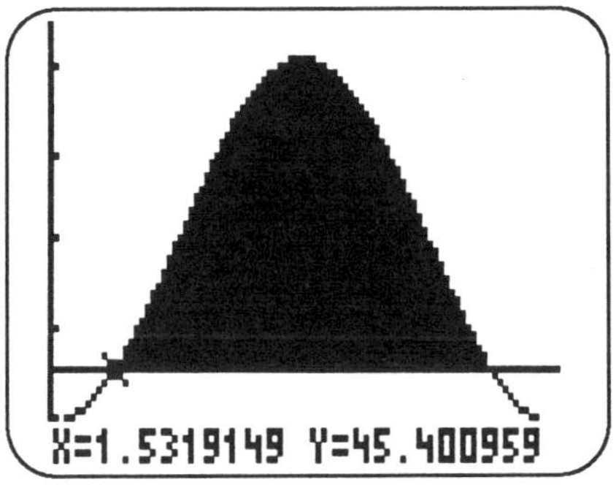

- By pressing the Zoom key and Trace features you can zoom in on the point(s) of intersection. If you have used the colon to separate the graphing statements, the shading will reappear on the graph.

Additional Problems

1. The surface area of a cylindrical can which holds 1000 cm^3 can be written as a function of the radius r. The function is $S(r) = 2\pi r^2 + \frac{2000}{r}$. For what value of r is the surface area less than 650 cm^2?

2. The formula for finding the payment on an installment loan is given by

$$P(L, r, n) = \frac{rL(1+r)^n}{(1+r)^n - 1},$$

where L is the amount of the loan, r the monthly interest rate, and n the number of monthly payments. If $L = \$10,000$ and $r = 0.0125$, for how many months should you take out a loan so that the payments are less than \$250 per month?

SECTION 3

Polynomial and Rational Functions

Investigating Graphs of Polynomials

Because polynomial functions only involve simple addition and multiplication, including raising real numbers to integral powers, it is relatively easy for us to work with them. In trying to find a relationship between two quantities, we usually turn first to polynomial functions. When these fail, we may go on to other types of functions, but even these other functions often end up being approximated or modeled by polynomials. By being able to look at graphs of polynomial functions, we can observe several properties. These include

- the global behavior of the function and its graph,
- the local behavior, including zeros and turning points, and
- the relationship between zeros and factors.

Problem Statement

Graph each of the following polynomials. Look at the global behavior as well as the local behavior. Using the graph that shows the local behavior, estimate the zeros (to the nearest tenth) and record the number of turning points.

GRAPHING CALCULATOR SOLUTION. Start by setting the domain to $-10 \le x \le 10$ and the range to $-10 \le y \le 10$. Change the domain and range for the last two problems as directed here. Using this viewing window, you will see the global behavior of the following functions. Zoom in enough then to see the zeros and the turning points.

1. $y = x^3 - 3x^2 - 6x + 8$

2. $y = -x^3 + x^2 - 7x - 7$

3. $y = x^4 - 3x^2 - 12x + 5$

4. $y = x^3 - x + 1$

5. $y = x^6 - x^2 + 9$

6. $y = x^4 + 3x^3 + x^2 - 3x - 2$

7. $y = -2x^4 + 8x^3 - 6x - 1$

8. Set $-5 \leq x \leq 5$ and $-200 \leq y \leq 50$ for this problem.
$y = x^4 - 2x^3 - 19x^2 + 36x - 12$

9. Set $-5 \leq x \leq 5$ and $-100 \leq y \leq 50$ for this problem.
$y = x^5 - 3x^4 - 10x^3 + 18x^2 + 24x$

Additional Problem

Based on your observations, write a concise statement of the relationship between the degree of a polynomial, the number of zeros, and the number of turning points. Also, write about the role of the leading coefficient and the constant term in the graph of the polynomial.

Turning Point Algorithm: Locating Maximum and Minimum Points

Problem Statement

The post office allows for the girth plus the length of a package to be up to 108 inches. If we assume that a rectangular package has a square base and perpendicular sides, what is the maximum volume the package can have?

GRAPHING CALCULATOR SOLUTION. If we can find a function for the volume of the package with the given parameters, we can graph it and use the trace and zoom features to estimate the greatest volume.

- Let the girth be $4x$ and the length l. Then we know that $4x + l \leq 108$. The volume will be $x^2 l$, or $x^2(108 - 4x)$. On a new line or on a clear screen, enter the function definition and then press [SHIFT] [0] ([F] MEM) [F1] (**STO**) and [1] to store the function as f_1.
- Determine an appropriate domain for x. Obvious choices are $x \geq 0$ and $x \leq 27$. Why? Since we don't know the range, start with $0 \leq y \leq 15000$.

Set the domain and range and graph the function. Use the [Trace] feature to move to near the maximum point of the function.

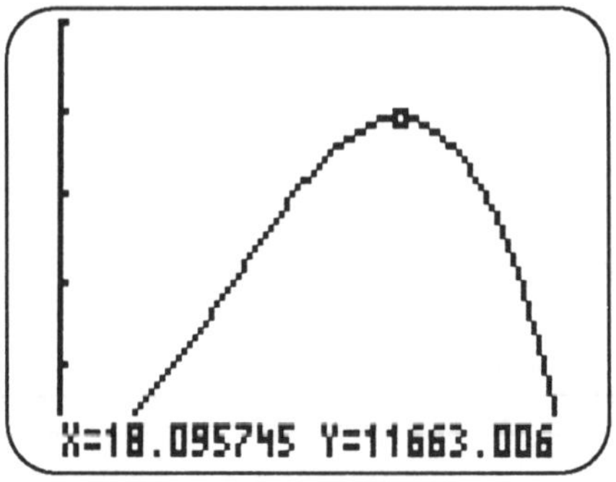

- Press [Zoom] and select the box option [F1] **BOX**. Move the cursor slightly to the left and above the maximum point. Press [EXE]. Now move the cursor slightly to the right and below the maximum point. As soon as you press [EXE], the calculator will use the zoom box you have just defined as the new graphing window.
- You can now retrace and zoom again, each time increasing the resolution of the points and getting a better estimate for the maximum point. Your graph may vary somewhat from this one, depending upon how far you move the cursor in defining the new graphing window.

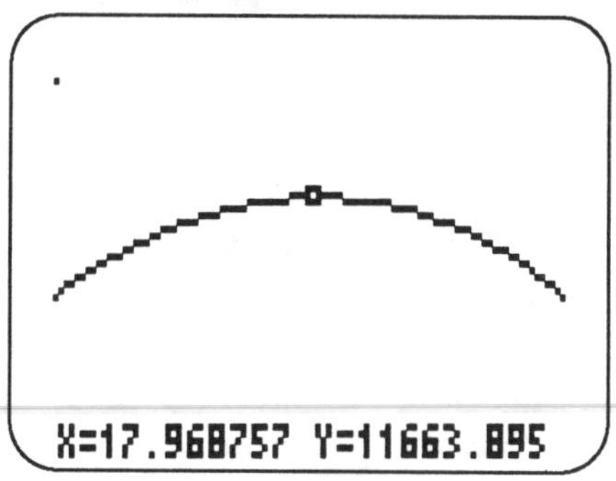

PROGRAMMING SOLUTION. There is a nice algorithm that will find the maximum point to a prescribed degree of accuracy. You can include it in a program that will automatically find the numerical approximation for the extreme point.

The algorithm requires you again to define the function and graph it to get some idea where the maximum occurs. Using the x-coordinate of a point to the left

of the maximum point, the algorithm steps up using a prescribed step size until the function begins to decrease. It then backs up a couple of steps and starts the process again, this time using a smaller step size.

The following program initially steps up by tenths, and each time it begins again, the step size is decreased by a factor of 10. Once two successive x-coordinates are within the prescribed degree of accuracy, the program stops.

Note. This program is set up to find a maximum point. By changing the first > to a < sign, you could use the same program to find minimum points.

Program Code: MAXMIN

Program Code	Comments
'MAXMIN'	
1 →S	
"PT. LEFT OF MAX–MIN"? →B	
Lbl 1	Begin loop to locate turning point.
.1×S →S	Set initial step size.
Lbl 2	Begin loop to check for increasing function.
B →A	Set left endpoint (B) equal to A.
A + S →B	Set right endpoint equal to $A + S$.
A →X	Store A as X.
f_1 →W	Store $f(A)$ as W.
B →X	Store B as X.
f_1 →Z	Store $f(b)$ as Z.
Z > W ⇒Goto 2	Determine if $f(x)$ is still increasing. If so, go to 2.
A – S →B	If not, back up a step, store $A - S$ as B.
Abs (A – B) > .1x^{y}5 ⇒Goto 1	If A and B are too far apart, go to 1.
A ◢	Display the x-coordinate of the point.
f_1 ◢	Display the y-coordinate of the point.

With the program written and saved, you are ready to execute it. Press [MODE] [1] to return to **RUN** mode.

- Be sure you have entered the function as f_1.
- In order to run a program, press [SHIFT] [Range] (**PRGM**) [F3] (**Prg**) and the number or letter of the program.

- Press [EXE] and input a value to the left of the maximum point. The program will display the x-coordinate of the maximum point when the left and right points are within 0.1^5. Then press [EXE] to see the y-coordinate of this point. The program will be more accurate if the power is increased to a number greater than 5.

Additional Problems

1. Assume the base of the package (in the above problem) is a circle with diameter x instead of a square. Write the function for the volume and find the maximum volume of this package.
2. Three major cities are located on a grid system with coordinates $(0,-10)$, $(10,5)$, and $(20,-15)$. The telephone company wants to put a switching station along a road that follows the x-axis of the grid system and lay cable in straight lines from the station to the each of the three cities. Where should they place the station to minimize the length of cable required?

Zero-Finding Algorithms

Problem Statement

We want to form an open rectangular box by cutting squares from the corners of an 18 by 24 inch rectangle and folding up the flaps to form a box. We need a box that holds 624 cubic inches.

GRAPHING CALCULATOR SOLUTION. To find when the function $f(x) = x(18-2x)(24-2x)$ equals 624, graph $f(x)$, and $g(x) = 624$. By tracing and zooming, we can approximate the point(s) of intersection.

- Enter $x(18-2x)(24-2x)$ and press [SHIFT] [0] ([F] MEM) [F1] (**STO**) and [1] to store this functions as f_1. Press [AC] and enter 624. Store this function as f_2.
- Set the range so that $0 \leq x \leq 9$ and $0 \leq y \leq 1000$.
- On a new line or a clear screen, press [Graph] [SHIFT] [0] ([F] MEM) [F3] (f_n) and [1] to recall the first function. Without pressing [EXE], press [EXE] [SHIFT]. Now press [SHIFT] [Graph] [0] ([F] MEM) [F3] (f_n) and [2] to recall the second function. Now press [EXE]. Use the **Trace** feature to move the cursor to the point(s) of intersection.

- By pressing the [Zoom] key and selecting [F1] (**BOX**) you can zoom in on the point(s) of intersection. You must use the colon between the graphing statements in order to see both functions when you zoom. (Your graph may vary from the one shown here, depending on how your calculator is set and your choice of zoom box.)

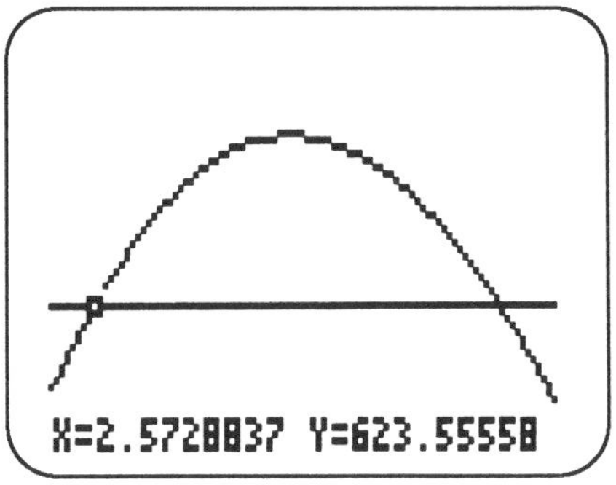

Frequently, the first step in solving an equation is to set one side of the equation equal to zero.

- To do this on the calculator, define f_3 to be $f_1 - f_2$. First, press [SHIFT] [0] ([F] MEM) [F2] (**RCL**) and [1] to recall the first function, press [−], and press [SHIFT] [0] ([F] MEM) [F2] (**RCL**) and [2] to recall the second function. Now store this as f_3 by pressing [SHIFT] [0] ([F] MEM) [F1] (**STO**) and [3].
- Set the range so that $0 \le x \le 9$ and $-100 \le y \le 100$. Store these range values and graph function f_3.
- Again, use the **Zoom** and **Trace** features to locate the zero(s) of equation f_3.

Programming Solutions. There are two nice algorithms that can easily be programmed into the Casio and used to find the zero(s) of equations. Like many numerical algorithms, both have limitations, but used carefully, they can find many approximations for zeros of equations for which analytical solutions are difficult or impossible.

Bisection Algorithm. The Bisection Algorithm begins by taking two x-coordinates, one with a positive y-coordinate and one with a negative y-coordinate. By finding the midpoint between these two x-coordinates, finding the y-coordinate of the midpoint, and replacing the original point whose y-coordinate has the same sign, this algorithm continually bisects the interval on the x-axis until the endpoints of the interval are as close is desired.

Program Code: BISECT

Program Code	Comments
'BISECT'	
"LEFT ENDPOINT ="? →A	Enter a point to the left of the zero.
"RIGHT ENDPOINT = "? →B	Enter a point to the right of the zero.
Lbl 1	Begin loop.
A → X	Assign A to X.
f3 → M	$f_3(A)$ stored as M.
(A+B)÷2 → X	Find the midpoint.
f3 → C	Finding y-coordinate of midpoint.
CM ≤ 0 ⇒X →B	Replace B with X if the signs of their y-coordinates are the same.
CM ≥ 0 ⇒X →A	Replace A with X if the signs of their y-coordinates are different.
Abs(A−B) ≥ .1x^y10 ⇒Goto 1	If A and B are too far apart, go back to beginning of the loop.
"ZERO AT X ="	Display the zero.
X	

Before attempting to run this program, make sure that the function for which you are trying to find a zero is stored as f_3. To execute the program, return to **RUN** mode, and press [SHIFT] [Range] (**PRGM**) [F3] (**Prg**), select the number or letter of the program, and press [EXE]. You will need to input two values, one with a negative y-coordinate and one with a positive y-coordinate.

In general, what limitations may arise when using the Bisection Algorithm?

Secant Algorithm. A second algorithm works even when a zero is located at a point of tangency of the function and the x-axis, and it is usually faster than the Bisection Algorithm. This algorithm draws the secant line between two points on the function and then finds the zero of this line. By discarding one of the original points and replacing it with the point whose x-coordinate is the zero of the previous secant line, this algorithm will quickly zoom in on a zero of the function.

Program Code: SECANT

Program Code	Comments
'SECANT'	
"FIRST VALUE ="? →A	Input any x-value.
"SECOND VALUE = "? →B	Input any other x-value.
Lbl 1	Begin loop.
A → X	Store A in X.
f3 → W	Store $f_3(A)$ as W.
B → X	Store B in X.
f3 → Z	Store $f_3(B)$ as Z.
(Z−W)÷(B−A) → M	Find slope of segment AB.
A → B	
-W÷M+A → A	Let A equal the zero of the line AB.
Abs(W) ≥ .1x^y8 ⇒Goto 1	If A and B are too far apart, go to top of the loop.
"ZERO AT X ="	Display the value of the zero.
A	

Before attempting to run this program, make sure that the function for which you are trying to find zeros is stored as f_3. When you run the program you will need to input two values, but unlike the Bisection Algorithm, you do not need to make sure that the y-coordinates have different signs.

In general, what limitations may arise when using the Secant Algorithm?

Additional Problems

1. The cost of postage stamps has gone up exponentially in recent years. The cost function may be given by $c(t) = 0.04e^{0.065t}$, where t represents years after 1958. According to this function, when will the cost pass the \$0.50 level? the \$1.00 level?

2. The sales revenue from the sale of ski equipment is cyclic, roughly following the function $f(x) = 150 + 450\cos\left(\frac{\pi x}{6}\right)$, where x is months after January 1 and $f(x)$ is the revenue per day in dollars. Over what part of the year does the store sell more than \$500 of ski equipment per day?

Picard's Method: Locating Points of Intersection

Problem Statement

Find the point of intersection of the line $y = x$ and the parabola $f(x) = Rx(1-x)$. Try the following values of R ranging from 0.5 to 4.0. This is an easy problem to solve algebraically, but it does illustrate Picard's method nicely. Picard's Method, as an example of iteration, behaves unexpectedly. This section is more of an investigation of this behavior than a means of finding points of intersection.

GRAPHING CALCULATOR SOLUTION. Obviously we could graph the two functions and zoom in on the point of intersection. We will first use the recursive feature of the calculator to solve the problem.

- Enter an initial value for x, say 0.05. Do not store 0.05 as x, simply enter 0.05 and press [EXE].
- Now enter $1.5 \cdot$ [ANS] $\cdot (1 -$ [ANS]). Press [EXE].
- Each additional time you press [EXE] the previous answer is substituted back into the function. Press [EXE] until the successive values displayed don't change.

PROGRAMMING SOLUTION. We can use the following program to perform the above steps for us and at the same time generate a graphical display of the solution.

- What you will see when you run the program is the web diagram associated with the function. You pick some initial x-value and the program draws the vertical line to the point $(x, f(x))$, followed by the horizontal line to the point $(f(x), f(x))$. The program then goes into a loop, letting $f(x)$ from the last point plotted serve as the new x-coordinate. The process is repeated until either the point of intersection is found or a preset number of iterations is preformed without finding the point.
- First let $f_1 = X$ and $f_2 = 0.5X(1 - X)$.
- Enter the program in **WRT** mode and then run the program. At the prompt, enter an initial value for x. An initial guess of around 0.1 usually works well.

Program Code: PICARD

Program Code	Comments
'PICARD'	
Cls	
"INPUT R VALUE" ? → R	
RANGE -.1, 1.1, .2, -.1, R ÷ 3.5, .1	Set viewing window for each *R*-value.
"INPUT INITIAL X"? →A	
Graph Y = f_1	
Graph Y = f_2	
Plot A,0	Plots first point.
A →X	
f_2 →B	Finding $f(x)$.
Lbl 1	Begin loop.
Plot A,B	
Line	Drawing vertical lines.
Plot B,B	Plots points on line $y = x$.
Line	Draws horizontal lines.
B →A	Store B as A.
A →X	
f_2 →B	Store $f(A)$ as B.
Abs(A−B) ≤ .1x^y11 ⇒Goto 2	If A is close enough to B, jump out of loop.
Goto 1	If not, go back through main loop.
Lbl 2	
Plot A,B	Plot final point.
A ◢	Show final value of x.
"PRESS G-T"	Press this key to toggle between text and graph.

With the program written and saved, you are ready to execute it.

- Be sure you have entered the function as $f_1 = X$, and $f_2 = RX(1 - X)$.
- Enter a value for R. Use values for R between 0 and 4.
- Now run the program. Press [SHIFT] [Range] (**PRGM**) [F3] (**Prg**) and press the number or letter of the program.
- Press [EXE] and input an initial value for x. If the point of intersection is an attraction point, the web will spiral into the point. With repelling points the web will move out from the point of intersection.

- When (or if) the programs stops running, press [G↔T] to see the graph and the point of intersection. You will discover that some web diagrams don't appear to converge or diverge but seem to bounce around forever. You might want to add steps to the program to limit the number of times it goes through the loop before stopping. If the program does not stop on its own, you may need to press [AC] to break the execution. You can still toggle to the graph to see what is happening.

The figures below show the graphical output from the above program. The graph on the left shows the web diagram for $R = 2.5$ while the one on the right is for $R = 3.5$. The values generated in the first graph approach the point (0.6, 0.6) while the values on the right seem to bounce around and never approach one number. Experiment with the value of R and see if you can determine the values for which the algorithm **a.** converges to one value, **b.** bounces between 2 values, and **c.** bounces between 4 values. You may have slightly different graphs if you began with a different range.

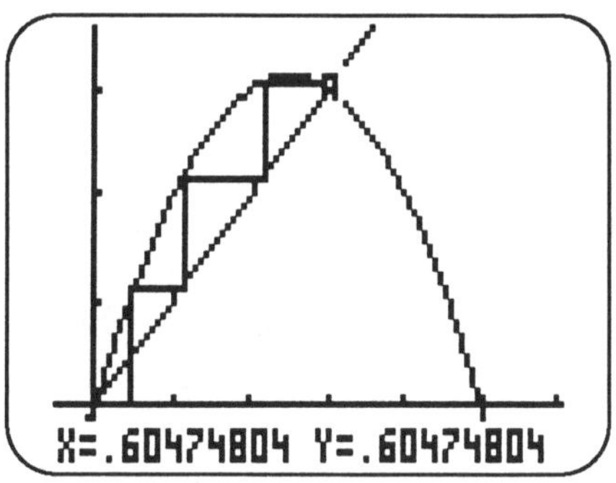

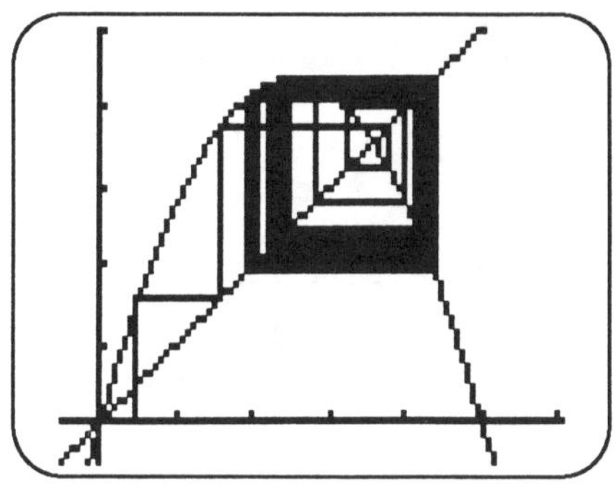

Additional Problems

1. Find the point of intersection of $y = x$ and $y = \cos x$.

2. Solve $3x = e^x$ using Picard's Method. **Hint.** By graphing, you will see that there are 2 solutions. First, use $y = x$ and $y = \frac{1}{3}e^x$. Then use $y = x$ and $y = \ln 3x$.

3. Solve $x^2 = \cos x$ using Picard's Method.

Graphs of Rational Functions

Problem Statement

Graph the rational function

$$f(x) = \frac{x^2 - x - 6}{x - 1}.$$

Examine the global and local behavior.

Graphing Calculator Solution. By looking at the equation of $f(x)$ we notice that the function is undefined at $x = 1$. Long division shows us that

$$f(x) = x + \frac{-6}{x - 1}.$$

- Set the domain to be $[-5, 5]$ and the range $[-20, 20]$.
- Enter the function in either form and store it as f_1.
- Graph the function on the given domain and range.
- We clearly see that the graph of $f(x)$ is approaching the vertical asymptote $x = 1$ as the x-values approach 1. Tracing along the curve will convince you that as x approaches 1 from the right, y approaches negative infinity and as x approaches 1 from the left, y approaches positive infinity. Here is the graph.

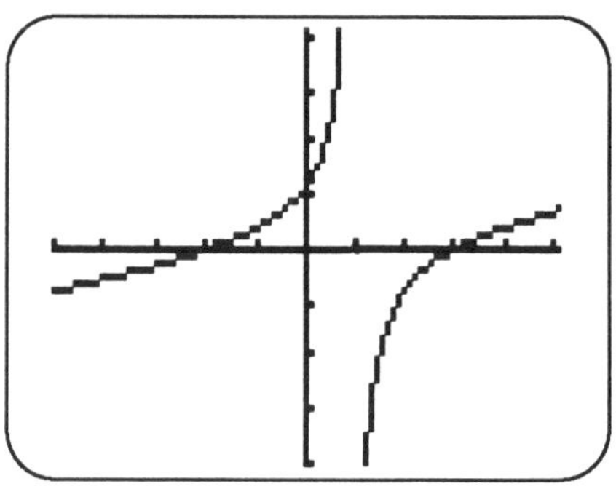

Now let's explore what $f(x)$ looks like as x gets very large or very small; in other words, let's look at the global picture.

- Reset the domain to be $[-50, 50]$ and the range $[-50, 50]$.

- Graph the function using this new domain and range.

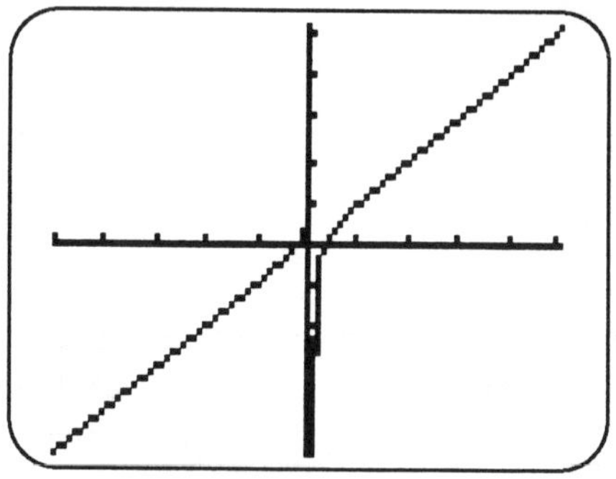

- We see now that the graph of $f(x)$ looks very much like the graph of the line $y = x$. Tracing along the function shows that it is very close to being $y = x$. Why does this graph look linear and the first graph not?

Asymptotes. Normally a rational function can have two of three types of asymptotes. Horizontal and oblique are relatively easy to see when looking at a global picture of the graph. The vertical asymptotes are more difficult to see. In the above example, the line $y = x$ is an oblique assymptote and $x = 1$ is a vertical asymptote.

Additional Problems

Find appropriate windows to view both the local and global behavior of the following rational functions.

1. $f(x) = \dfrac{3x}{x-2}$.
2. $g(x) = \dfrac{x^2 - 5x + 1}{x-2}$.
3. $h(x) = \dfrac{x^2 - x - 6}{x-3}$.
4. $k(x) = \dfrac{x^3 - x^2 - 3x + 3}{x-2}$.
5. $l(x) = \dfrac{x}{x^2 - 4x}$.

Fitting a Polynomial to Data Points

Problem Statement

How many triangles can you form by connecting n points in a plane (no three colinear)?

Graphing Calculator Solution Using Lagrange Interpolation. One technique for solving problems is to consider simple examples of the problem and find a pattern. In this problem, the simplest case involves 3 points, and there is only one triangle. Four non-colinear points can be connected to form 4 triangles, 5 points will form 10 triangles, and 6 points will form 20 triangles. To try to find a polynomial function that contains the given points, we can use a method called Lagrange Interpolation. The process is simple. By finding a polynomial which contains one point but equals zero at each of the x-coordinates of the other points, we will have n polynomials of degree $n-1$, where n is the number of given points. By adding these polynomials together, we have one polynomial which will pass through all of the given points. We will use this polynomial to predict the number of triangles formed by connecting n points as in the problem above.

Construct the following polynomials:

$$f_1 = (X-4)(X-5)(X-6)$$
$$f_2 = (X-3)(X-5)(X-6)$$
$$f_3 = (X-3)(X-4)(X-6)$$
$$f_4 = (X-3)(X-4)(X-5)$$

When f_1 is evaluated at $X = 3$, the value is -6, but we want it to be 1.

$$\begin{aligned} f_1 &= (3-4)(3-5)(3-6) \\ &= (-1)(-2)(-3) \\ &= -6. \end{aligned}$$

We will need to put a coefficient into f_1 to make $f_1(3) = 1$. Go back and add the coefficient $\left(-\frac{1}{6}\right)$ to f_1.

$$f_1' = \left(-\frac{1}{6}\right)(x-4)(x-5)(x-6).$$

In a similar manner, $f_2(4) = 2$, $f_3(5) = -2$, and $f_4(6) = 6$. Inserting coefficients of 2, -5, and $\frac{10}{3}$ into f_2, f_3, and f_4 respectively, we have the desired polynomials. Adding these together yields a polynomial which now passes through all the given points.

Note that there is no guarantee that the polynomial that fits through these 4 points will necessarily be the function that predicts the number of triangles that can be formed using the n points, but this polynomial will pass through the 4 given points. A proof that this function solves our original problem would need to be done, perhaps using induction.

The polynomial that fits through the 4 points is the sum of f_1 through f_4, but, since most of the graphing calculators have limited symbolic capabilites, we can't find the simplest form of this polynomial with the calculator. We can, however, use the sum to graph and predict other values of the function. Whenever we fit a polynomial through points with exact coordinates using this technique, there will be no residuals. The graph below shows the graphs of f_1 through f_4 on the same graph using a viewing window of $+2 \leq x \leq 7$ and $-3 \leq y \leq 12$.

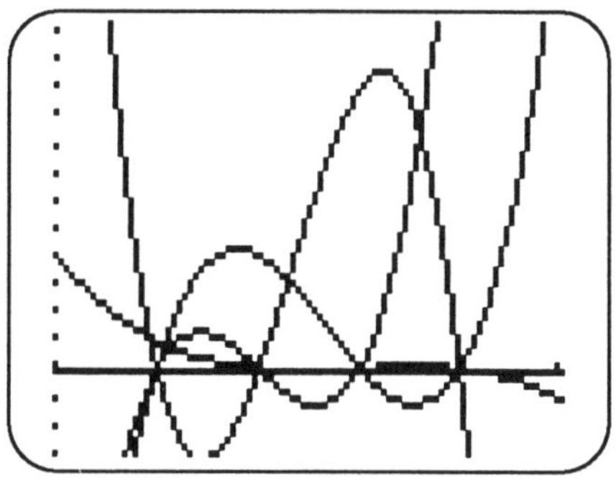

Add functions f_1 through f_4 and store as f_5. The graph of this function is shown below. Enter an integer value and store it in X and the recall function f_5 and notice the integer value for Y. Use a viewing window with $2 \leq x \leq 11.4$ and $-10 \leq y \leq 160$.

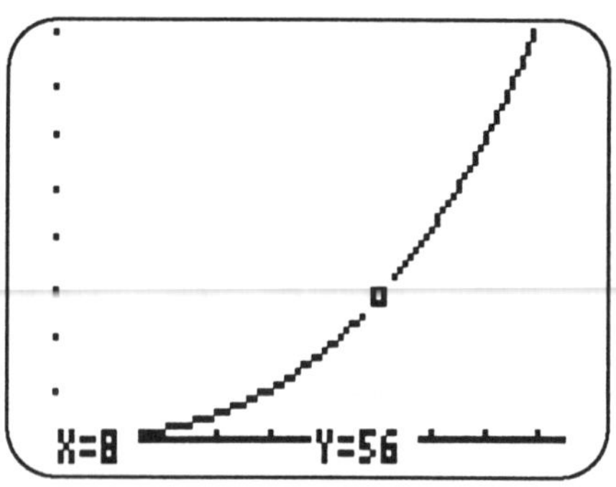

Additional Problem

1. An airline has terminals in n cities and would like to have at least one flight each day connecting every possible pair of cities. How many such routes are there?

SECTION 4

Exponential and Logarithmic Functions

The Naturalness of e

Problem Statement

Normally banks compound interest on a regular basis. If this is done only once a year, the *stated interest* is the true or *effective interest.* If, on the other hand, the interest is compounded more than once a year, the effective annual rate is greater than the stated rate. What happens when the interest is compounded over shorter and shorter periods of time? (The formula for compound interest appears on p. 11.)

GRAPHING CALCULATOR SOLUTION. Enter the expression $(1 + .06 \div 1)^1$ into the calculator and press EXE key. The return on \$1.00 is \$1.06, or a 6% rate of return.

Now press the left arrow once to recall the expression and use the left arrow again to change the expression to $(1+.06\div 2)^2$. This will give the effect of compounding twice during the year. Press EXE and notice the return.

Press the up arrow and increase the number of times the interest is compounded. Notice that while the effective rate changes, it does seem to be approaching some limit. As the length of the compounding period approaches zero and the power approaches infinity, the expression $(1 + .06 \div n)^n$ approaches a limit.

Is there a simple way to arrive at this limit? To understand the limit, go back and change the expression to $(1+1\div n)^1$ and repeat the process. The expression $(1+1\div n)^n$ eventually gets closer and closer to the number e. In fact, e is defined as this limit.

Now go back and enter the expression $(1 + .06 \div 100)^{(100 \div .06) \times .06}$. As you increase the number of compounding periods, what value does this expression approach? What would be another way to write this limit?

Additional Problems

1. What is the effective rate earned if the stated rate is 6% and interest is compounded monthly?
2. What is the effective rate earned if the stated rate is 8% but interest is compounded continuously?
3. Compare the function $f(x) = e^{0.06x}$ to the function in the text above, $g(x) = (1 + .06 \div n)^{nx}$. Graph the two for small values of n, and then for increased values of n.

Exponential and Logarithmic Functions

Problem Statement

You just won $100,000 in the lottery and you decide to deposit half of the winnings into a bank account which pays 7% compounded annually. How much will you have in the account at the end of 3 years? At the end of 20 years?

Solution Using Recursion. The Casio *fx*-7700 stores the last result as **Ans** each time the [EXE] key is pressed. This is useful since compound interest is recursive; that is, based on the previous balance.

- Since banks truncate to 2 decimal places, the solution would be more realistic if the calculator were set to 2 decimal places. Press [SHIFT] [2] (DISP) [F1] (**FIX**) [2] and [EXE].
- Enter 50000 and press [EXE].
- Now press [Ans] [×] [1] [.] [0] [7] (Ans × 1.07) and press [EXE]. This total is the balance at the end of one year.
  - — Press [EXE] again. This total is the balance at the end of 2 years.
  - — Press [EXE] again. Each time you press [EXE] you will see the balance at the end of another year.
- Continue this process until you find the balance at the end of 20 years.

Solution Using a Formula. The future value of a compound interest problem is given by the formula $F = 50000(1.07)^n$, where n is the number of years.

- To find the balance at the end of 3 years, press [50000] [×] [1.07] [x^y] [3] [EXE].
- To find the balance at the end of 20 years, press the left arrow. This places a copy of the formula on the screen. Use the arrows to change the 3 to a 20 and press [EXE].

Solution Using Functions. The above formula for future value of a compound interest problem can be entered as a function.

- Enter the formula 50000×1.07^x, the press [SHIFT] [0] ([F] MEM) [F1] (**STO**) [1].
- Press [AC] and store the value 3 as X, press [3] [→] [X, θ, T] [EXE]. Now press [SHIFT] [0] ([F] MEM) [F3] (fn) [1] [EXE].
- To see the result at the end of 20 years, repeat the above process after storing 20 as X.

Solution By Graphing. Since we have entered the formula for compound interest as the function f_1, we can graph the function and trace along the curve.

- Press [Range] and set the domain $0 \le x \le 23.5$ and range $50000 \le y \le 200000$.
- Press [Graph] [SHIFT] [0] ([F] MEM) [F2] (**RCL**) [1] [EXE].
- Now press [F1] (**Trace**) and use the right and left arrows until you get to the points where $x = 3$ and $x = 20$. You can press [Zoom] and [Trace] to get increased accuracy.

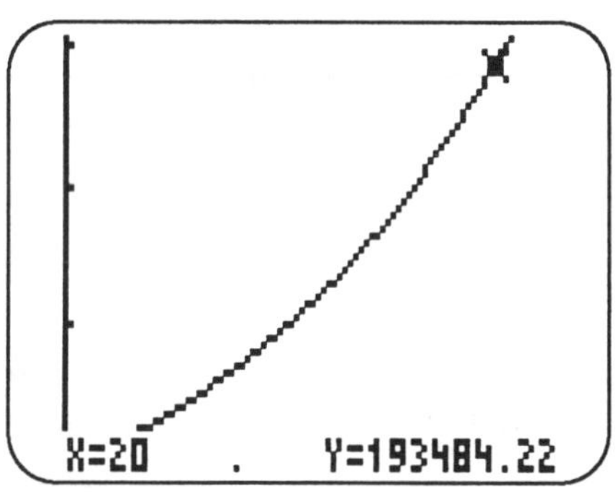

Additional Problems

1. If the \$50,000 were invested at 7% compounded annually, how long would it take for the amount in the account to first go over \$250,000?

2. If your parents set up an education fund for you the day you were born depositing \$1700 in an account earning 10% compounded annually, how much will you have for college when you turn 18?

Annuity Problems

Problem Statement

When you start out in business for yourself, you know that you will need to set up your own retirement plan. You start out by saving \$200 each month in an individual retirement account through a mutual fund which has been paying an average of 9% per year for the past 20 years. If you assume that the fund will continue to pay at the same rate, how much will you have in the account at the end of 30 years?

GRAPHING CALCULATOR SOLUTION. You deposit \$200 into the account and it earns 0.75% (9% divided by 12) during the first month. At that point you add another \$200. This process will be repeated each month for the next 360 months. The calculator will do this nicely using recursion.

- First enter 200 and press [EXE]. This \$200 will be stored as the last answer **Ans**.
- Now press [Ans] [×] 1.0075 then add 200. The line should look like **Ans** × 1.0075 + 200.
- Press [EXE]. Notice that the answer is \$401.50. Now each time you press [EXE], the calculator will repeat the last line entered into the calculator. After you press [EXE] ten more times, you have \$2501.52. This represents the total in the account as soon as you make the twelfth deposit.
- You could press [EXE] 348 more times, but this is obviously not the best way to finish this problem.

PROGRAMMING SOLUTION. You can use recursion for solving this problem by writing the above steps of the graphing calculator solution into a programming loop.

Program Code: ANNUITY

Program Code	Comments
'ANNUITY'	
"NO. PAYMENTS"? →J	Enter number of payments.
J−1 →J	
"INITIAL DEP."? →A	
"PERIODIC DEP."? →D	Periodic deposit.
"RATE"? →R	Interest rate for the deposit period.
A →B	Initial balance.
Lbl 1	Begin loop.
B×(1+R)+D →B	Add interest to balance and add deposit.
Dsz J	Decrease J by 1 until it equals zero.
Goto 1	End loop.
B	Display balance.

Store and run the program. After a short time the calculator will display the total in the account: $366,148.70.

FUNCTION SOLUTION. If we could write a single, closed-form formula or function we could compute the total in the account at the end of any given period of time without having to find the amount at the end of each previous time period. If you write the above steps and look for the pattern, you should be able to come up with the following function.

$$f(x) = \frac{(200)(1.0075^x - 1)}{0.0075}$$

- Enter this formula and store it as function f_1. Press [SHIFT] [0] ([F] MEM) [F1] (**STO**) [1] [EXE].
- Now to store 360 in X, press 360 [→] [X, θ, T] [EXE].
- Now recall the function by pressing [SHIFT] [0] ([F] MEM) [F3] (f_n) [1] [EXE]. The function will be evaluated using the current value of X.

The advantage of the function solution, in addition to being much shorter than the first two methods, is that you may easily change the function and the number of months. The first solution requires less algebra but much more time. The second solution also requires less algebra, but some programming ability. However, there are recursive functions or relations for which closed form equations are either

difficult or impossible to derive. Therefore, a knowledge of the solutions using recursion is valuable.

Additional Problems

1. How much would you have in an account if you saved $250 a month for 10 years given an annual interest rate of 9%, compounded monthly?

2. How much would you have in an account if you saved $50 a week for 10 years given an annual interest rate of 9%, compounded each week?

3. Assume that you have retired with savings of $750,000 and wish to pay yourself $50,000 per year. If the balance is left to accrue interest at 8% compounded yearly, how much would you have left in 20 years? Surprised?

4. In a problem in the last section, some parents invested $1700 in an account paying 10% compounded annually. In addition to the initial $1700, suppose they also invest $600 per year into the account. How much would be in the account at the end of 18 years? (**Hint.** Think carefully about the total number of payments being made.) If the interest were compounded monthly and they put $50 per month into the account, how much would the account yield?

SECTION 5

Curve Fitting: Linear Regression and Nonlinear Data

Linear Data and the Least Squares Line

Problem Statement

The serum cholesterol level in the blood is directly related to the percentage of fat calories in the diet. Given the following set of data, find the relationship.

% fat calories	9	11	14	16	22	25	31	35	38	39
cholesterol (mg/100 ml)	140	146	152	171	180	192	205	212	246	241

First plot the ordered pairs using the Scatter Plot Program. If the ordered pairs of data appear linear, you can fit the least squares line to the data and use this line to express the relationship between the level of cholesterol and the percent fat calories. The least squares line is the most common linear regression model.

- To graph the regression line, first compute the linear regression coefficients. To do this from the scatter plot, press [MODE] [÷] [F6] (**CAL**) to calculate the regression parameters. Press [F6] (**REG**) to see these parameters. A is the y-intercept, B is the slope, and r is the correlation coefficient of the regression line. On a new line or clear screen, enter the equation $BX+A$ and store this as function f_3.
- Before attempting to draw the scatter plot, be sure to set the range to accommodate your data. The plot that follows uses $5 \leq x \leq 45$ and $125 \leq y \leq 250$.
- To see the scatter plot with the regression line, press [Graph] [SHIFT] [F4] (**LINE**) [1] [EXE]. This line is the linear least squares regression line. You could also recall function f_3 and graph it. **Note.** If the data is linear or

nearly linear, you may not see the data points. Because of the resolution of the screen, they may be hidden by the line. Also, your graph may vary slightly from this one if you used different settings on the calculator.

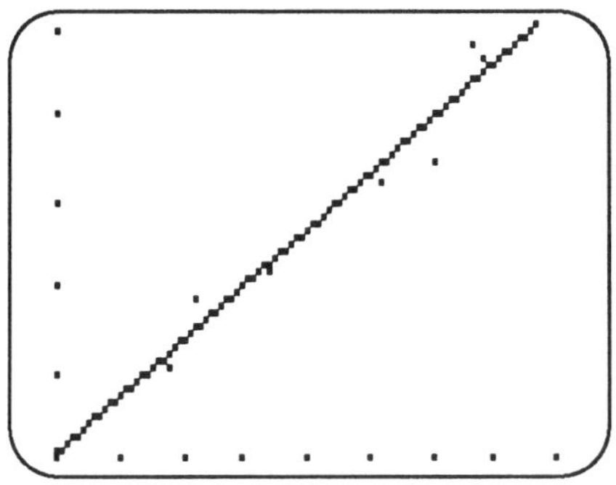

Additional Problem

1. A track is inclined at various angles and the time for a ball to roll down the trough is recorded. Plot the data and determine the relationship between the time (in seconds) and the angle of inclination (in degrees).

Angle	8	12	16	20	27	30	33	36	38	41	44
Time	2.05	1.63	1.53	1.10	0.90	0.88	0.80	0.69	0.57	0.49	0.36

   a. Use the calculator to find a linear equation which models the relationship between the angle and time.

   b. What does the slope of the linear model represent in terms of the relationship between the angle and time?

   c. Use the model to predict the time for an angle of 24 degrees.

   d. Using the model, estimate the angle of incline if the ball takes 1.0 second.

   e. Is the model a good model? Discuss its strengths and weaknesses.

The best way to determine how well a regression line fits the data is to look at the residuals; unfortunately, many graphing calculators will not allow you do this without writing a program. If you want to use your calculator to look at the residuals, you may use the residual program in Section 1 to find residuals for the linear regression function f_3 or use some data analysis software to study the residuals.

Scatter Plots with Transformed Data

Problem Statement

The highway patrol uses a formula for determining how fast a car in an accident was traveling, based on the length of the skid mark. The formula includes a factor for the type of road surface. If the highway department starts using a new road surface, the highway patrol needs to determine the formula for the new surface. Under controlled conditions test drivers stop cars on this surface at the following speeds and record the following skid distances.

speed in mph	20	25	30	35	45	50	55	60	65	70	80	90
skid length in feet	15	23	33	45	75	93	112	133	156	181	240	300

CALCULATOR SOLUTION USING LINEARIZED DATA. Enter the data using the data-entry/scatter-plot program and notice that the data points are not linear. As is the case with many data sets, the relationship between the variables is not linear and so the scatter plot is not linear.

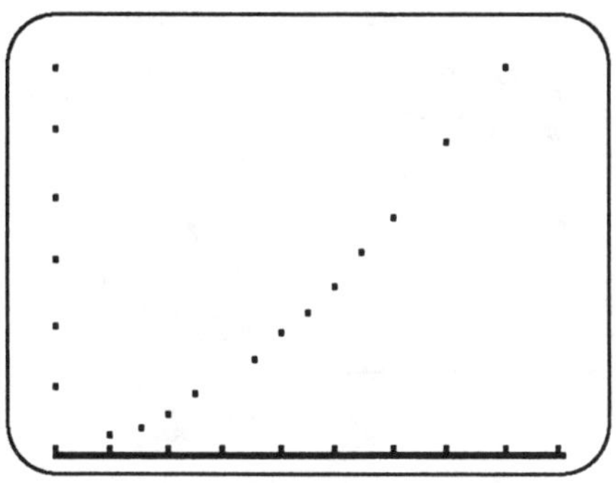

If we could linearize the data, then we could fit a line through the re-expressed data. The following program will make it possible to specify two functions, one to transform the x-coordinates and one to transform the y-coordinates. The program will transform, or re-express, the data and plot the transformed data on a scatter plot.

Since this data appears to be quadratic, we could either take the square root of the y-coordinates leaving the x-coordinates alone, or square the x-coordinates while leaving the y-coordinates alone. To take the square root, define and store $f_1 = X$ and $f_2 = \sqrt{X}$.

Program Code: REEXPRES

Be sure to set the mode to the regression mode (Press [MODE] [÷].) and the linear regression mode (Press [MODE] [4].) before entering this program.

Code	Comments
'REEXPRESS'	
Cls	Clear the graphing window.
Scl	Clear the statistics memory.
999999 →E	Place holder for minimum X.
-E →F	Place holder for maximum X.
E →C	Place holder for minimum Y.
-E →D	Place holder for maximum Y.
21 →B	Initial value for counter.
Lbl 1	Begin loop.
E[B] →X	Stored x-data stored in X.
f_1 →E[B]	X's transformed using f_1.
E[B] < E ⇒E[B] →E	Determining new Xmin.
E[B] > F ⇒E[B] →F	Determining new Xmax.
E[B+A] →X	Stored y-data stored in X.
f_2 →E[B+A]	Y's transformed using f_2.
E[B+A] < C ⇒E[B+A] →C	Determining new Ymin.
E[B+A] > D ⇒E[B+A] →D	Determining new Ymax.
B+1 →B	Adding 1 to counter.
B < A+21 ⇒Goto 1	End of loop.
.1(F−E) →G	
.1(D−C) →H	
Range E−G,F+G,G,C−H,D+H,H	Setting the range
21 →B	Reinitialize counter.
Lbl 2	Begin plotting loop.
E[B],E[B+A] DT	Storing transformed data.
Plot E[B],E[B+A]	Plotting data points.
B+1 →B	Add 1 to counter.
B < A+21 ⇒Goto 2	End of plotting loop.
Plot E,C	
"PRESS G-T"	

- After the program is entered, press [MODE] [1] to return to the **RUN** mode and store the program.
- Before running the program, be sure to clear all data by pressing [MODE] [÷] [F2] (**EDIT**) [F3] (**ERS**) [F1] (**YES**).

- The program will also transform the domain and range using the same transformation.
- We are now ready to run this program. Press [SHIFT] [Range] (**PRGM**) [F3] (**Prg**) and enter the number or letter of the program. Press [EXE] and the program will transform the data and plot the new scatter plot.

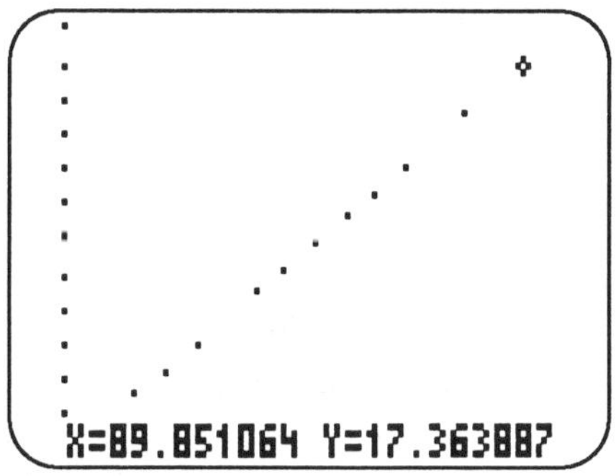

- Since the re-expression did linearize the data, the data was quadratic. We can now fit the least squares line through these re-expressed points using linear regression. To do this, follow these steps:
  - Press [G↔T] to return to the text screen. Press [F6] (**CAL**) [F6] (**REG**) [F2] (B) [X, θ, T] [+] [F1] (A) and store the linear equation as f_3.
  - Press [Graph] [SHIFT] [F4] (**Line**) [1] [EXE].

The equation for the least squares line through the re-expressed y-coordinates is $y = -0.02489 + 0.19295x$. (To see the residuals for this linear model, run the **RESIDUAL** program.) This line fits the linear data, so $y = (-0.02489 + 0.19295x)^2$ should fit the original data. The figure on the left shows the data restored to its original form. The figure on the right shows the fit of the model (function) to the data. To duplicate these graphs you must store the quadratic equation as f_3, restore the data to the original form, and graph this function with the data.

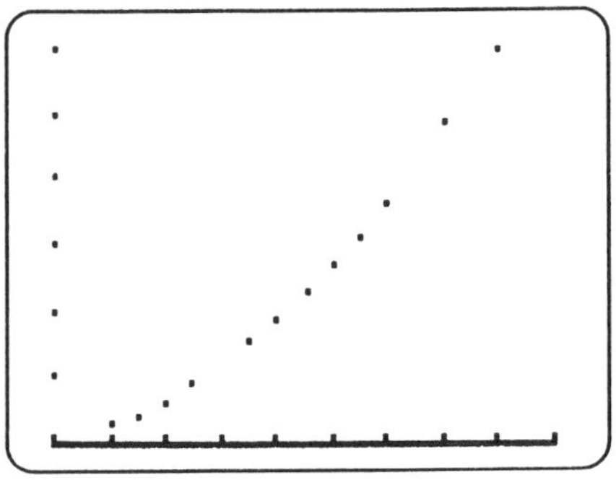

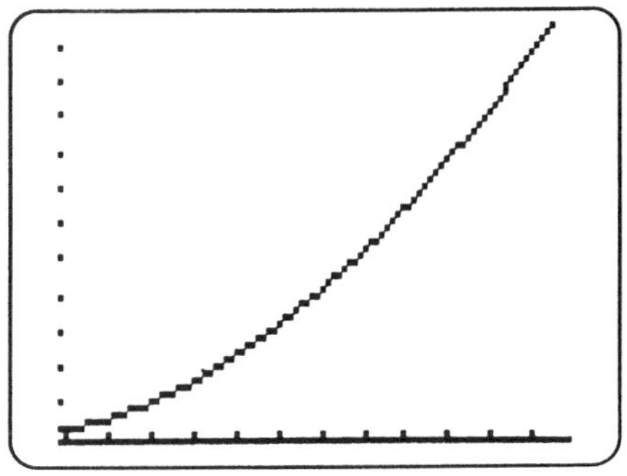

- In order to determine if the fit is as good as it looks, we need to examine the residuals. With the function $y = (-0.02489 + 0.19295x)^2$ stored as f_3, running the **RESIDUAL** program produces the following results. The figure on the left shows the residuals while the figure on the right shows the range of these residuals. Actual results will vary depending on whether or not you round the coefficients before graphing.

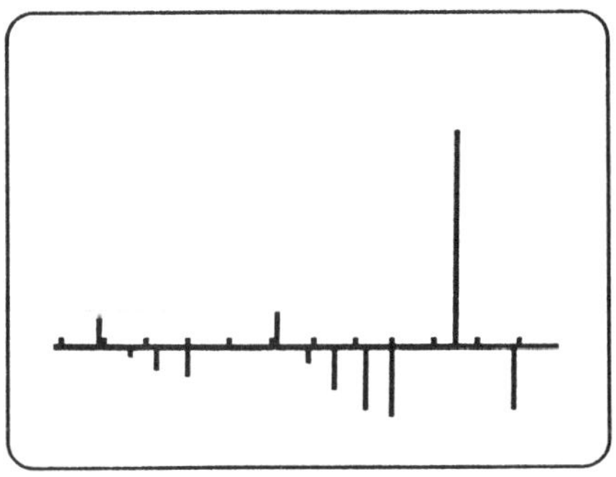

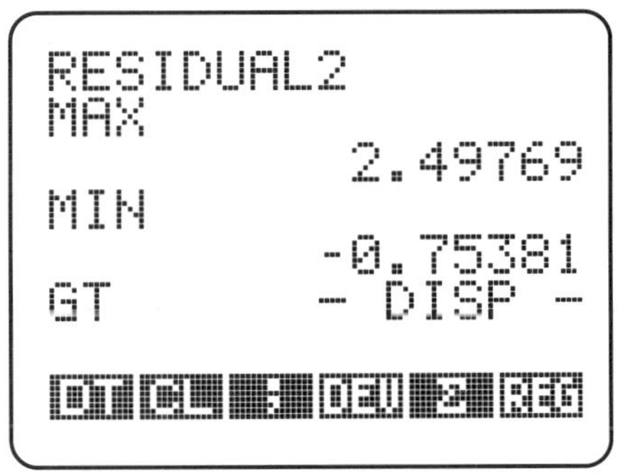

Additional Problems

1. The cost of going to college is rising faster than the general cost of living. The following table gives the Consumer Price Index (one measure of the cost of living) and the average cost (tuition and fees) for both public and private colleges over the past 10 years. Find exponential models for the CPI, the cost of public colleges, and the cost of private colleges as functions of time and compare the rates of growth.

Year	1981	1982	1983	1984	1985	1986	1987	1988	1989	1990
CPI	90.9	96.5	99.6	103.9	107.6	109.6	113.6	118.3	124.0	130.7
Public	909	1031	1148	1228	1318	1414	1537	1646	1781	1809
Private	4113	4639	5093	5556	6121	6658	7116	7722	8446	9391

Source: U. S. Department of Education, National Center for Educational Statistics

2. The rate at which oxygen is consumed by animals, in ml/sec, is related to the animal's body mass. Several representative data points are given in the following table

Mass (kg)	.006	.03	1.1	3.1	5.2	10.3	30.0	100	170	300
Oxygen (ml/sec)	.016	.058	1.08	2.50	3.80	6.61	15.7	41.7	64.1	101

a. Plot the data and determine the nature of the relationship between the oxygen rate and body mass.

b. Find a relationship which linearizes the data.

c. Fit a line through the linearized data and determine the slope and intercept.

d. Find a model which approximates the original data.

SECTION 6

Trigonometry

Toolkit of Trigonometric Functions

Problem Statement

Most periodic phenomena can be modeled by some form of the basic trigonometric functions. The basic sine function forms a sinusodial wave, and all of the other trigonometric functions can be defined in terms of the sine function. The tides, electrical currents, temperature, and daylight cycles are all examples of phenomena that can be modeled by sine waves. Let's investigate the basic trigonometric functions on the calculator.

GRAPHING CALCULATOR INVESTIGATIONS. The basic sine wave function has period 2π and amplitude 1. Enter [sin] [X, θ, T] and store this function by pressing [SHIFT] [0] ([F] MEM) [F1] (**STO**) [1]. Now set the domain to be $-2\pi \leq x \leq 2\pi$ and the range to be $-3 \leq y \leq 3$. Press [Graph] [SHIFT] [0] ([F] MEM) [F2] (**RCL**) [1] [EXE]. Two cycles of the graph of the sine function will be drawn.

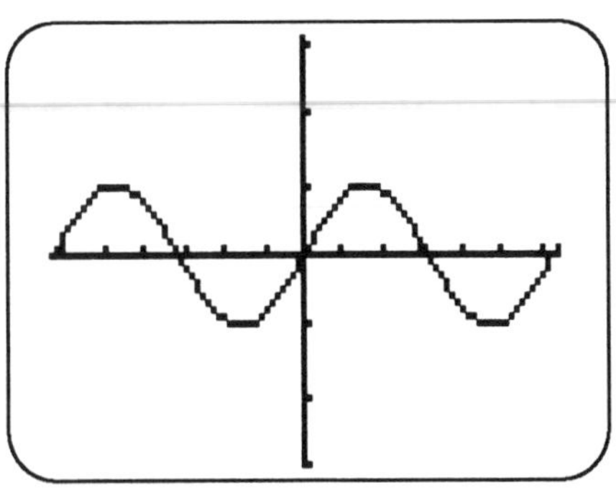

At this point go back and enter the cosine as function f_2. To see the graph of the cosine with the sine, remember that you need to enter both graph statements

separated by a colon. Press [Graph] [SHIFT] [0] ([F]MEM) [F2] (**RCL**) [1] [SHIFT] [EXE] [Graph] [SHIFT] [0] ([F]MEM) [F2] (**RCL**) [2] [EXE]. Notice that the cosine looks exactly like the sine, except that it is shifted horizontally.

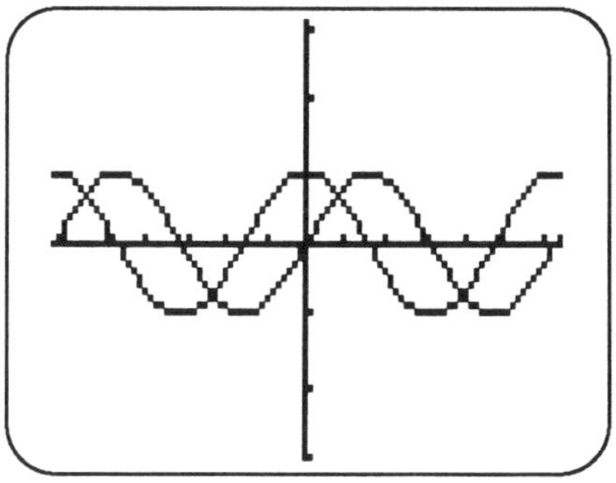

It appears that the cosine is simply the sine shifted to the left by one-fourth of a cycle, or $\frac{\pi}{2}$. Enter $\sin(x + \frac{\pi}{2})$ as function f_3. Clear the existing graphs by pressing [F5] (**CLS**) with the graphing screen showing and then repeat the steps above to graph the cosine and the $\sin(x + \frac{\pi}{2})$. Notice that the two graphs are identical.

The other four trigonometric functions are combinations of the sine and/or cosine. The tangent is the ratio of the sine to the cosine. Clear the previous graphs then go back and replace f_3 with $\sin(x) \div \cos(x)$ and graph this function. Notice where the tangent is zero, where it equals 1, and where it is undefined.

Repeat the above process with $f_3 = \cos x \div \sin x$. This ratio is defined as the cotangent. It is, of course, the reciprocal of the tangent. The secant is simply the reciprocal of the cosine.

Let $f_3 = 1 \div \cos x$ and graph f_3. Notice the range, where the function equals the cosine, and where it is undefined. Now repeat this process with the reciprocal of the sine. The resulting function is called the cosecant.

The Sine and Cosine as Circular Functions

Problem Statement

The sine and cosine functions can be defined as the coordinates of points on the unit circle. The argument or independent variable of both functions is the distance in a counter-clockwise direction along the circumference of the unit circle from the point (1, 0). If this distance value is paired with the first coordinate of the point on the unit circle, the cosine function is formed. If the second coordinate

of the point on the unit circle is paired with the distance, the resulting ordered pairs form the sine function.

GRAPHING CALCULATOR SIMULATION. The parametric graphing capabilities of the Casio fx-7700G can be used to show the relationship between the points on the unit circle and the sine and cosine functions. The following procedure will draw both the unit circle and the graph of the sine or cosine function. Follow the steps below to see this relationship.

- Press the [MODE] [SHIFT] [×] keys to enter the **PARAM** mode. Be sure you are also in radian mode. Press [SHIFT] [1] (**DRG**) [F2] (**Rad**) [EXE].
- Now press [cos] [X, θ, T] and store this as f_1. Press [AC] and enter [sin] [T] and store this as f_2. Enter [T] and store this as f_3 and finally store [sin] [T] as f_4.
- In order to plot the unit circle and the sine or cosine, we need to set the ranges for X, Y, and T. Press the [RANGE] key and set the parameters as follows:

Xmin :	-1
max :	2π
scl :	1
Ymin :	-2.5
max :	2.5
scl :	1
T,θ	
min :	0
max :	2π
ptch :	.05

- To graph the unit circle and the sine function follow these steps:
  - Press [Graph] (**Graph(X,Y)=(**) [SHIFT] [0] ([F] MEM) [F3] (f_n) [1] [SHIFT] [→] (,) [SHIFT] [0] ([F] MEM) [F3] (f_n) [2] followed by [)] [SHIFT] [EXE].
  - On a new line press [Graph] (**Graph(X,Y)=(**) [SHIFT] [0] ([F] MEM) [F3] (f_n) [3] [SHIFT] [→] (,) [SHIFT] [0] ([F] MEM) [F3] (f_n) [4] followed by [)] [EXE].
- Notice that the unit circle is plotted along with the sine function. Each y-coordinate of the sine function is the same as the y-coordinate of the point on the unit circle.

- Press the [F1] (**Trace**) key and [▲]. Notice the value of the parameter T and the values of x and y as you use the right arrow to trace around the circle. The value of T is the radian measure, or distance around the unit circle, the x is the cosine for that value of T, and the y is the sine. Pressing the up-arrow again will yield the corresponding point on the graph of the sine function. Here the value of T and x will be the same and the value of y will be $\sin(x)$.

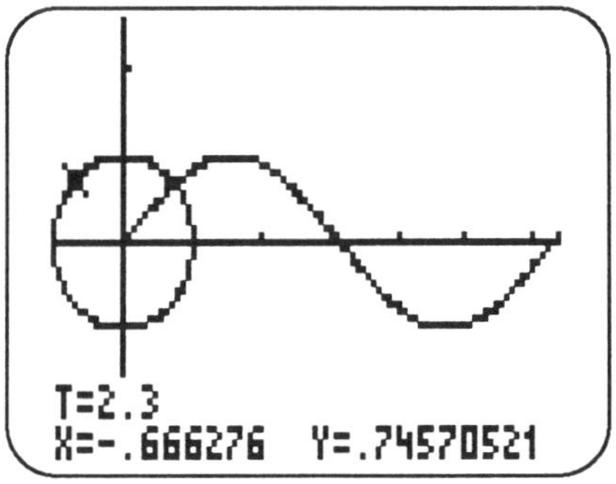

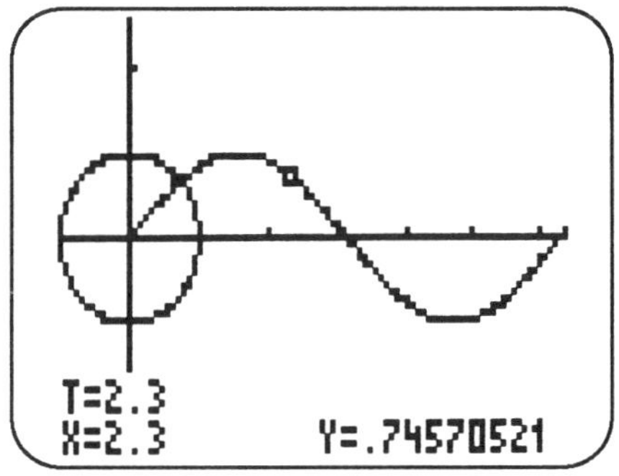

- To see the unit circle and the cosine graphed simultaneously, clear the graph from the screen and go back and change f_4 to cos T, and repeat the above steps. In the figures below it is more difficult to see that the y-coordinate of the cosine on the left is the same as the x-coordinate of the point on the unit circle in the figure on the right. Use the [Trace] key and the arrows to again see the relationship between the unit circle and the cosine function.

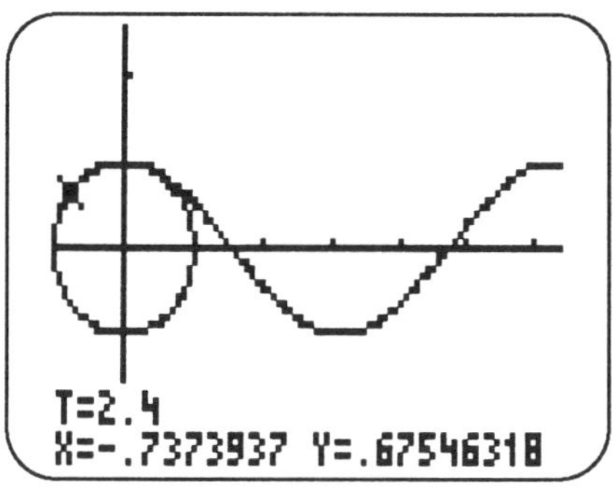

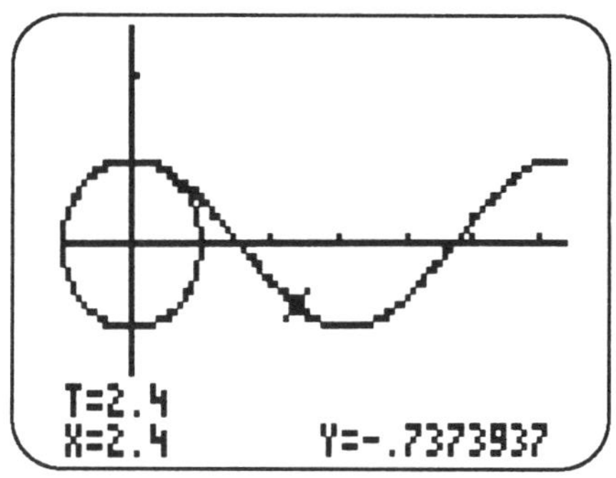

Advanced Graphing Lab

Problem Statement

Let's observe the transformations of functions formed by adding and multiplying by constants. Then, in the second part of the lab, we'll observe what happens when we add and multiply functions.

GRAPHING CALCULATOR SOLUTION. Use your calculator to investigate the following. Make notes and draw conclusions. You may need to change the mode. Press [MODE] [+] (**COMP**) and [MODE] [SHIFT] [+] (**REC**).

- Graph $y = A\sin(x)$. Store various values in A and note the effect the A has on the graph of $y = \sin(x)$.
- Graph $y = \sin(Bx)$. Since this function is periodic, it is easy to see what effect B has on the graph. Discuss this transfomation.
- Graph the function $y = \cos(x - C)$. Store various values in C and note the effect C has on the graph of the normal cosine function.
- Graph the function $y = x\sin(x)$. What effect does the x have on the graph of $y = \sin(x)$? Graph $y = x$ and $y = -x$ on the same axes with $y = x\sin(x)$. What do you notice?
- Graph $y = 2 + \sin(x)$. What effect does adding 2 have on the graph of $y = \sin(x)$.
- Now graph $y = x + \sin(x)$. Explain the effect of adding the x to $\sin(x)$. Now graph $y = x$ on the same axes as $y = x + \sin(x)$. Make some generalizations about the effect of adding functions.
- Use the conclusions from above to sketch graphs of $y = x\cos(x)$, $y = |x| + \sin(x)$, and $y = e^x + \sin(x)$. Use your calculator to check your graphs.

Additional Problems

1. The approximate hours of sunlight in Durham, North Carolina for the 21st of each month are given in the following table. Find a sine curve which predicts the hours of sunlight for any given day of the year.

Month	Jan.	Feb.	Mar.	Apr.	May	June
Sunlight	10.08	11.06	12.18	13.34	14.22	14.65
Month	July	Aug.	Sept.	Oct.	Nov.	Dec.
Sunlight	14.20	13.33	12.20	11.04	10.09	9.68

2. Alternating electrical current can be modeled by a sine function. Write the function for an alternating current with a frequency (the reciprocal of the period) of 60 Hz (60 cycles per second) and an amplitude of 220. Graph the function over 2 cycles.

3. To create waves with various shapes in producing electronic music, a process called FM feedback is used. A wave is produced, fed back into the function and this new signal is then fed back into the function again. Graph the functions $f(x) = \sin(2x)$ and $g(x) = \sin(x + f(x))$. Now graph $g(g(x))$ and $g(g(g(x)))$. What shape does the wave seem to be approaching?

SECTION 7

Matrices

Matrix Operations

Problem Statement

The Burger Barn has two stores in Durham. Both stores sell three types of sandwiches: hamburgers, chicken fillets, and fish fillets.

In September, Store I sold 512 hamburgers, 209 chicken sandwiches, and 52 fish sandwiches. Store II sold 491 hamburgers, 192 chicken sandwiches, and 48 fish sandwiches. In October, Store I sold 623 hamburgers, 231 chicken sandwiches, and 72 fish sandwiches. Store II sold 578 hamburgers, 203 chicken sandwiches, and 62 fish sandwiches.

Store I charges $1.89, $1.79, and $1.59 respectively for burgers, chicken, and fish. Store II is located in an expensive mall, and its prices are higher: $1.95, $1.85, and $1.65.

What was the total number of each type of sandwich sold during the two months by each store? What was the change in the number sold of each type of sandwich? How much revenue did each store receive from selling sandwiches each month?

CALCULATOR MATRIX SOLUTION. While this problem could be solved by arithmetic, the data can be organized nicely and all of the questions answered using matrices. The Casio fx-7700G has two matrices, A and B, that you can assign values to and one, C, for storing answers.

- To work with matrices, you must be in **MATRIX** mode. Press [MODE] [0] for this mode and [MODE] [1] for the **RUN** mode.
- To enter values into matrix A, press [F1] (**A**) followed by [F6] (∇) [F1] (**DIM**) to change the dimension of the matrix. Change the dimension of matrix A to 2 by 3. Press [2] [EXE] [3] and [EXE]. You are now ready to enter the first piece of data in the first row, first column of matrix A.

Let the rows stand for the store number, and the columns for the types of sandwiches. Enter the data for the month of October in matrix A. Place 623, 231, and 72 in the first row and 578, 203, and 62 in row 2. Now press [EXE] after entering each value to store the data in matrix A.

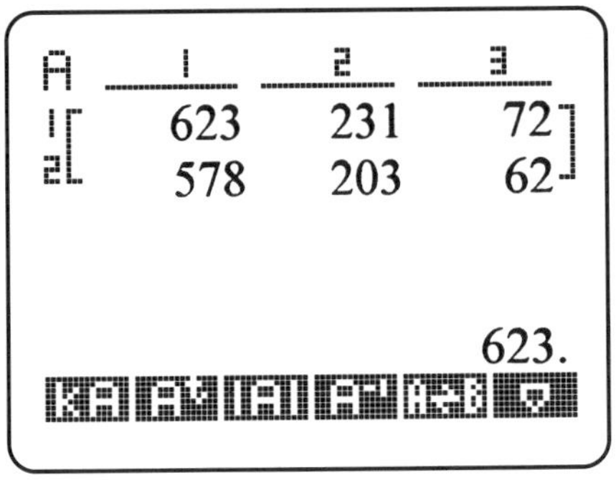

- To enter the September data into matrix B, press [PRE] followed by [F2] (**B**). Now repeat the above steps and enter the appropriate data by rows. This data will be stored in matrix B.
- To find the total number of each type of sandwich sold during the two months, we need to add entries. To do this press [PRE] followed by [F3] (+). The resulting 2 by 3 matrix will be the total for each sandwich by store. Notice that the matrix fits on the screen and that one value will be highlighted. This value will appear at the bottom of the screen using the display mode you have selected. If a matrix is too large to see on the screen, it may be necessary to use the arrow keys to see additional rows or columns.

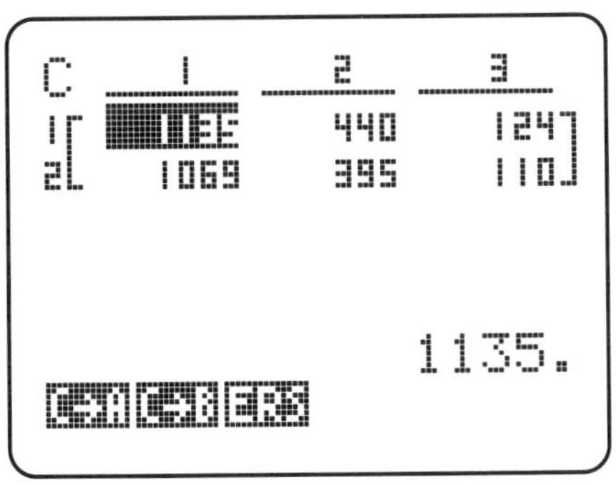

- To find the change from September to October, press [PRE] followed by [F4] (−). The resulting 2 by 3 matrix shows the change in the number of sandwiches by store.

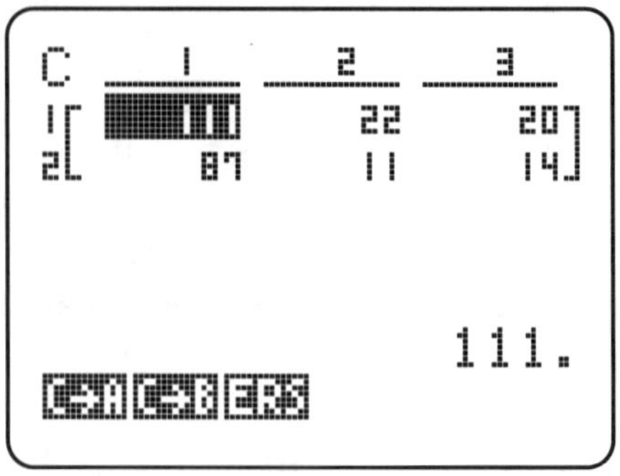

- To find the total revenue from sandwiches for both months, press [PRE] and add A and B again. This time store the resulting matrix in C by pressing [F1] (**C** $\rightarrow$**A**). Now it is necessary to store the price data in matrix B. Press [PRE] again and change the dimension of B to 3 by 2. Enter the hamburger prices in the first row, the chicken prices in row 2, and the fish prices in row 3 of matrix B. Now press [PRE] followed by [F5] to multiply the sum by the price matrix. The resulting 2 by 2 matrix has the desired information plus some extraneous information. What does the entry in row 1 column 2 give us? Row 2 column 1?

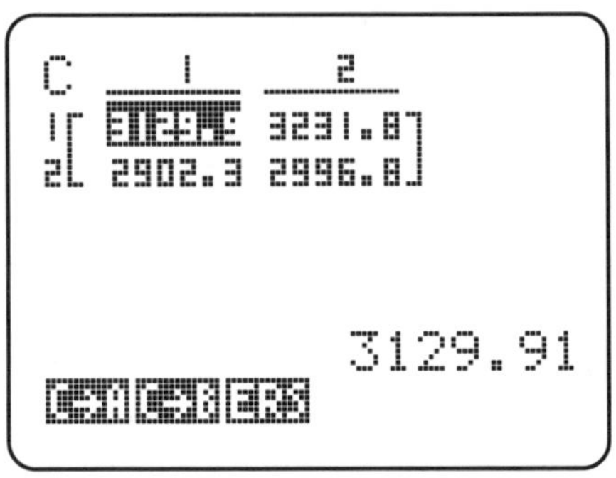

Powers of Square Matrices

Problem Statement. Planning for your eventual retirement, you decide to put the $10,000 your rich aunt gave you for graduation into a mutual fund and you further plan to put an additional $100 each month into the fund. This fund has historically yielded an average return of 9% per year (0.0075 per month.)

How much would you have in the account at the end of one year? At the end of 30 years?

CALCULATOR MATRIX SOLUTION. While this problem is usually not done with matrices, the matrix solution is nice. Annuity problems involve adding and multiplying, exactly the operations in matrix multiplication. On the Casio *fx*-7700G the process is complicated by the fact that you cannot raise a matrix to a power or use matrices in the programming mode.

- Define matrix A to be a 1 by 2 matrix with entries [10000 100] and matrix B as a 2 by 2 matrix with 1.0075 and 0 in the first row and two 1's in the second row.
- Multiply matrix A by B. How did the first entry get to be $10175? What does this quantity represent?

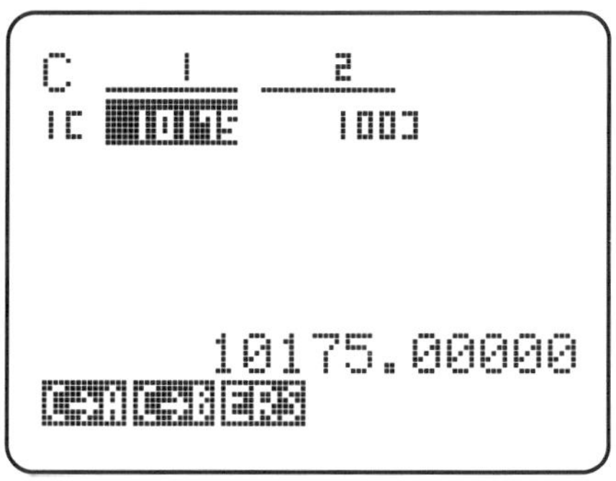

- One way to find the amount at the end of 12 months, is to store the result of the above multiplication as matrix A by pressing [F1] and then press [PRE] to multiply this new matrix A by B again. This will yield the total in the account after the second installment of $100. Now each time you multiply, store the product in A and multiply again, you will get a matrix with the total amount in the account after an additional installment. This total will appear in the first row and first column.

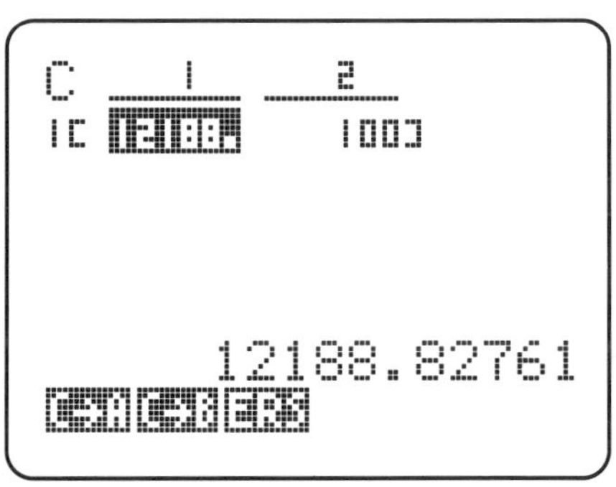

- To find the total in the account after 360 months, you would need to repeat this process 348 more times, or raise the original matrix B to the 360th power and then left-multiply by the original matrix A. Unfortunately, the Casio fx-7700G will not raise a matrix to a power nor can we write a program while in matrix mode. There is, however, a way around this problem, albeit a rather awkward one.

Since we can store the product of A and B in either A or B, we need to find the most efficient way to raise a matrix to a power using products. This is not too difficult if the product is a power of 2. If we wanted to know how much money would be in the account at the end of 256 months, the following scheme would work.

- Define both A and B to be 2 by 2 matrices containing 1.0075 and 0 in the first row and two 1's in the second row.
- Multiply these together and store the result in both A and B. To do this, first store the product in A by pressing [F1] and then press [1] [F1] to multiply the matrix A by the scalar 1, and finally store this result in B by pressing [F2]. At this point the original matrix has been squared and stored in both A and B.
- Multiply A and B again, and repeat the above steps, storing the 4th power of the original matrix in both A and B. By repeating this process six more times, you would have the 256th power of the original matrix. Store this as matrix B.
- Now go back and define A to be [10000 100] and multiply A by B. The resulting 1 by 2 matrix is [144686.22 100] and the first entry is the projected amount in the account at the end of 256 months.

If you need a power of a matrix that is not a power of 2, things get more difficult. The 360th power, however, is not as bad as some. Since $360 = 45 \times 8$, we can first multiply until we get A^5, store this in both A and B, and then continue to multiply A by B, but only store the product in B until B contains the 45th power of the original matrix. Then store this power in both A and B and multiply them together, placing the 90th power in both A and B. Repeat this two more times and you will have the 360th power of the original matrix. The steps to do this are as follows:

- Define both A and B to be 2 by 2 matrices containing 1.0075 and 0 in the first row and two 1's in the second row.

- After storing the data in the last matrix, press [PRE] and then [F5]. Press [F1] to store this result in A. Press [PRE] and repeat this process 3 more times. Be sure to store your last product C in A.

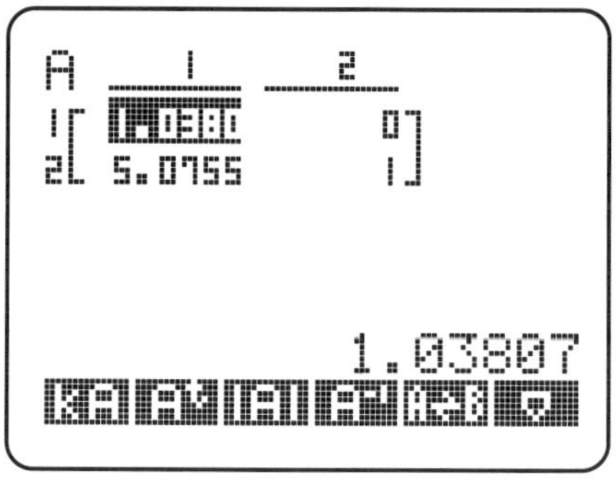

- Now press [1] and [F1]. This again gives the scalar product $1A$. Store this product in B by pressing [F2] (**C →B**).

- At this point the 5th power of the original matrix is store in both A and B. Now press [PRE] and [F5] and place the answer, the 10th power in A only by pressing [F1]. Press [PRE] [F5] [F1] 7 more times. At this point, store the 45th power in B by pressing [1] [F1] (**KA**) [F2] (**C →B**). This matrix should contain the values below.

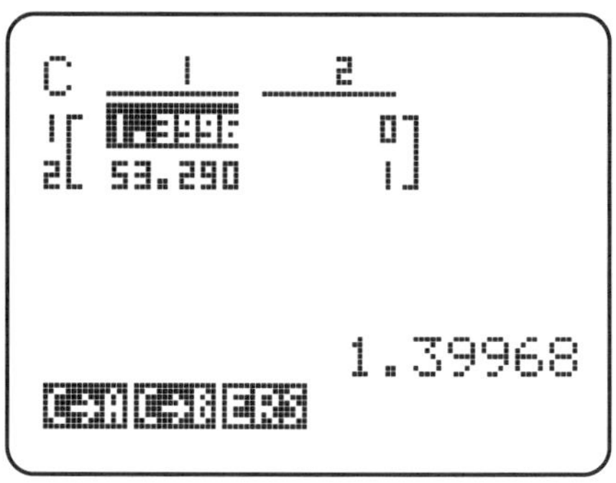

- After storing the 45th power in both A and B, press [PRE] and multiple A by B, storing the result, the 90th power in both A and B. Repeat this 2 more times. Store the 360th power in B. It should contain the following values.

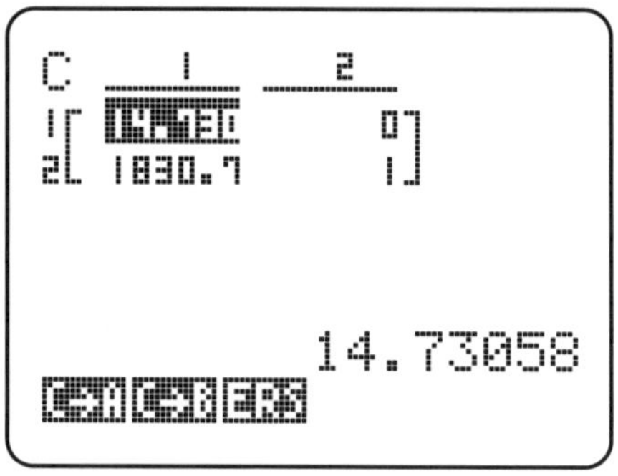

- Now go back and define A to be [10000 100] and multiply A by B. The resulting 1 by 2 matrix will be [330380.11 100].

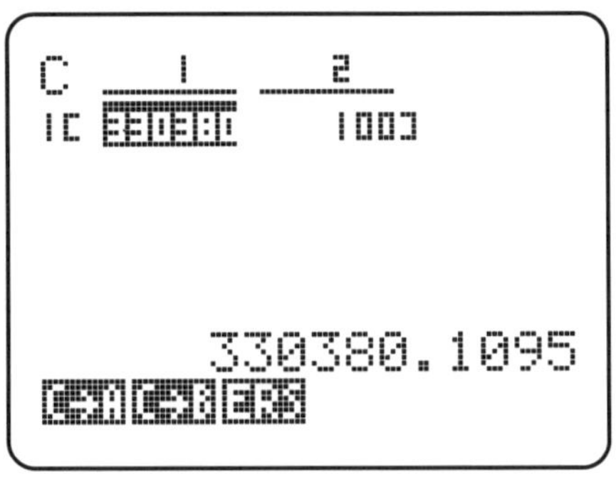

Additional Problems

1. Assume that at age 60 you retire and have managed to save $500,000. The account your money is in pays a 6% annual rate, compounded monthly. Being optomistic, you wish to withdraw the same amount each month from the account for the next 40 years. How much can you withdraw each month?

2. Upon reflection, you realize that inflation will cause your money to be worth less in the future, so you plan to withdraw a certain amount each month, and have that amount increase with inflation. You assume a 2% annual inflation rate.

   a. Now how much can you take out the first month?

   b. How much will you withdraw at age 100?

SECTION 8

Programming Hints

Programming Hints for the Casio fx-7700G Power Graphic Calculator

The following hints will acquaint you with the basic mechanics for writing programs. These hints are intended to teach simply the mechanics used to enter a program, rather than programming logic.

To write a program, follow these steps:

- First, determine the mode needed to run the program. For instance, if you are writing a program to plot data and draw the regression line, you need to be in the regression mode, probably using the linear regression model, using one of the two storage modes for data, and the draw mode for statistical graphs. These are the same modes you would need if you were not using a program to perform this task.
- After all of these other modes are set, press [MODE] [2] to enter the program write mode (**WRT**). The screen will look something like this:

```
   WRT    /  COMP
S-data     :  STO
S-graph :  DRAW
    981 Bytes Free
P0:'SCATTER'
P1:'MEDIAN'
P2:'RESIDUAL'
P3:'TABLE'
```

- The first line tells how much memory is left, and below is a listing of the programs. If there is no program entered under a number or letter, the **empty** prompt appears. You may arrow down to the program you wish to enter or edit, or select the program number or letter. Press [EXE] to enter the program.

You are now ready to enter the program.

If you are entering a new program, after you press the [EXE] key, the screen will be blank. For your own benefit, so that you can look at a list of your programs and know immediately which program is which, you should enter a title for the program. Press [SHIFT] [ALPHA] and notice the single quotation mark, the double quotation mark and the tilde. The single quotes are used in programming to enter comments. These comments **do not** appear when running the program. The double quotes are used for prompts in a program, and they **do** appear when the program is run. The tilde is used to indicate a range for variables.

Program statements are found under the **PRGM** menu. When you press [SHIFT] [Range] (**PRGM**) the menu looks like this:

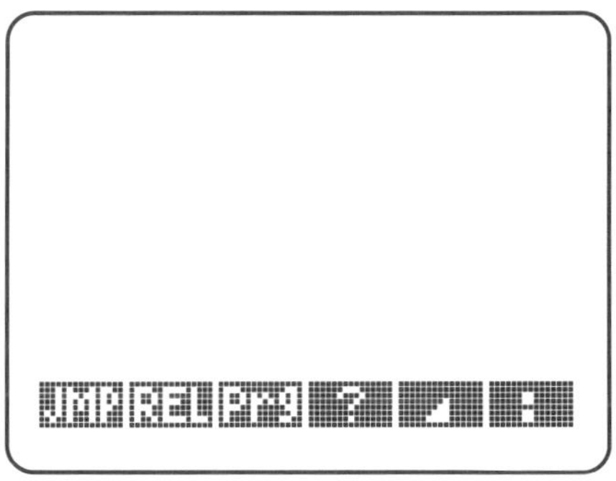

- Press [F1] (**JMP**) to see the commands under the jump menu. These are the commands used to construct jumps and loops in programs.

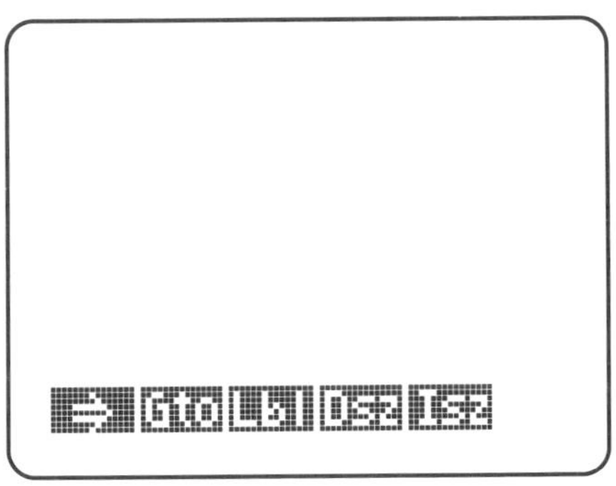

- Press [PRE] and then [F2] to access the relations needed to write test conditions in programs.

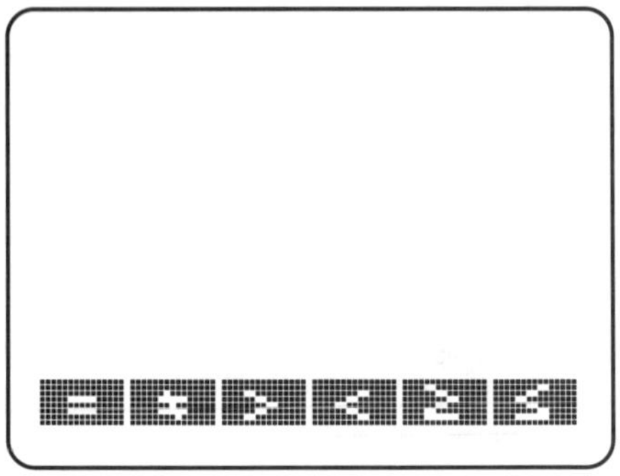

- Press [PRE] and notice the **PRG** menu item. This is used both to call and execute a program from within another program, or simply to execute a program from the **RUN** mode.

- The question mark (?) is used in programs as an input statement. It is used with the right arrow (→) to input a value and store as a variable. The statement **? →A** in a program would prompt the user to enter a value after the ? and then store this value in A.

- The ◢ symbol is used to display the value of the variable that precedes it in a program. The colon can be used to separate program statements when entering more than one statement per line. It is usually easier to read a program if one command per line is entered. As you write program lines, press [SHIFT] [EXE] and the next program command will start on a new line. This does not use any more memory, and clearly makes programs easier to read and edit.

Other symbols and commands are written into programs by pressing the same keys you would to activate the symbol or command in the normal execution mode. You will find programming easier if you are familiar with the keyboard and menus. Most of the symbols look just as they do on the keys or in the menus.

Many of the commands needed to program are found in the various menus. You can access these menus in or out of programming mode by pressing [SHIFT] and the keys with the green label above the key. The menus are listed below for your convenience.

SHIFT Graph (**MATH**). The Math menu has 4 submenus: **HYP**, **PRB**, **NUM**, and **DMS**.

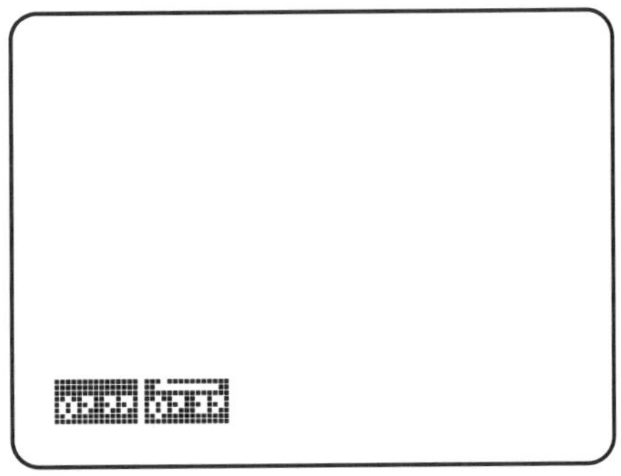

SHIFT 3 (**CLR**). This menu contains the following commands: **Mcl** to clear all value or variable memories; **Scl** to clear all statistical memories; **ARR** to clear matrices; and **PRG** to clear program memory. The first two of these commands can be used in programming.

[SHIFT] [0] ([F]MEM). This menu contains commands related to storing and recalling functions. There are 4 commands: **STO** to store a function; **RCL** to recall a function as the formula you entered; f_n to recall a function by name; and **LIST** to see a list of all of the function definitions. Only the middle two commands can be used in programming.

[SHIFT] [Range] (**PRGM**). The **PRGM** menus are explained in detail at the beginning of this section.

SECTION 9

Answers to Additional Problems

Answers to All Additional Problems

Page 3

1. The data does appear somewhat linear. If a line were used to model the data, the slope would be the change per year in the time to swim 100 meters.
2. The scatter plot shows that the relationship between life expectancy and the year born is nearly linear with a positive slope.
3. The scatter plot here appears somewhat linear, but to be realistic, it cannot continue to be linear. If it were to remain linear, it would eventually dip below two, then below one, and eventually less than zero. While small sections of many graphs may appear linear, there is often good reason why the entire relationship cannot be linear.

Page 10

1. The graphs of $y = c$, $y = |x|$, and $y = x^2$ are even functions.
2. The graphs of $y = x$, $y = x^3$, $y = \frac{1}{x}$, and $y = \sin(x)$ are odd functions.
3. Each of the toolkit functions is listed below with the actual domain and range as well as a suggested viewing window.

Function	Domain	Range	(Xmin,Xmax)	(Ymin,Ymax)
$y = c$	All reals	$y = c$	$(-10, 10)$	$(-10, 10)$
$y = x$	All reals	All reals	$(-5, 5)$	$(-1, 7)$
$y = \|x\|$	All reals	$y \geq 0$	$(-10, 10)$	$(-10, 10)$
$y = x^2$	All reals	$y \geq 0$	$(-5, 5)$	$(-5, 25)$
$y = x^3$	All reals	All reals	$(-5, 5)$	$(-25, 25)$
$y = \frac{1}{x}$	$x \neq 0$	$y \neq 0$	$(-5, 5)$	$(-5, 5)$
$y = \sqrt{x}$	$x \geq 0$	$y \geq 0$	$(0, 25)$	$(0, 5)$
$y = e^x$	All reals	$y > 0$	$(-5, 5)$	$(-2, 16)$
$y = \ln x$	$x > 0$	All reals	$(-2, 16)$	$(-5, 5)$
$y = \sin(x)$	All reals	$-1 \leq y \leq 1$	$(-2\pi, 2\pi)$	$(-2, 2)$

4. On the Casio fx-7700G, you must enter three functions and graph them together. Store the three functions as: $f_1 = 4, [-10, -2]$, $f_2 = X^2, [-2, 2]$ and $f_3 = 4, [2, 10]$. Be sure to set the domain to $-10 \leq x \leq 10$ and you should graph all three functions together using the colon to separate the graphing statements.

Page 12

1. At 8% it only takes 8 years and 9 months for money compounded monthly to double. At 6.5% it takes 10 years and 9 months.

2. The projectile stays in the air the longest when the angle is 16 degrees (to the nearest degree). At this angle the projectile has a range of 93.8 meters. You can use tables of values or graphs of the height and horizontal distance to see that this is the maximum range.

3. a. The function approaches 500 as t gets large.
   b. The function reaches 250 at approximately $t = 13.863$.
   c. From the graph and the table of values, you can see that the greatest change in the values of the function occurs near $t = 13.863$. This is also the point on the graph with the greatest slope.

Page 14

1. It appears that the graphs are shifted horizontally c units: to the left if $c > 0$; to the right if $c < 0$.

2. From these graphs it appears that the function is compressed (if $c > 1$) or stretched ($0 < c < 1$) in the horizontal direction. If $c < 0$ the same is true but the graph is flipped across the y-axis.

3. The parameter c stretches ($c > 1$) or compresses ($0 < c < 1$) the graph in the vertical direction. Again, if $c < 0$ the graph is flipped, but this time across the x-axis.

4. The graph of $g(x)$ looks as if it has been moved 1 unit to the right, stretched by a factor of 3 in the vertical direction, and moved up 2 units.

Page 16

1. One way to think of $f(x)$ as a composition is to write it as $g(h(x))$ where $h(x) = x^2 - 2$ and $g(x) = \frac{1}{x}$. The domain of $h(x)$ is all real numbers, but in the composition, an x value of $\pm\sqrt{2}$ will make the denominator zero. The domain of the composition will be all reals not equal to $\pm\sqrt{2}$.

2. Let $f(x) = g(h(x))$, where $h(x) = 9 - x^2$ and $g(x) = \sqrt{x}$. The domain of $h(x)$ is all real numbers, but when $x > 3$ or $x < -3$, the values of $h(x)$ are negative. Since the square root function is not real-valued for negative x, we must restrict the domain accordingly. The domain of $f(x)$ then is $-3 \leq x \leq 3$.

3. Let $f(x) = g(h(x))$, where $h(x) = \sin(x)$ and $g(x) = |\frac{1}{x}|$. The domain of $h(x)$ is all real numbers, but when $x = k\pi$ (k an integer) the sine is zero so these values of x cannot be used in the composition. The domain of $f(x)$ then, is all real numbers not equal to $k\pi$.

4. Let $h(x) = |x| - 2$ and $g(x) = x^3 - 1$. The domain of $h(x)$ is all reals, and $g(x)$ will accept all of the resulting y-values.

5. The composition $f(g(x)) = 6x + 3$ while the composition $g(f(x)) = 6x - 1$. Based on only this one problem, one might hypothesize that compositions of linear functions are linear (true) and that composition is not a commutative operation (also true).

Page 20

1. If you graph the function for the surface area and the constant function $y = 650$, the graphs intersect at roughly $x = 3.485$ and $x = 7.97$. Therefore the surface area is less than 650 when $3.485 < x < 7.97$.

2. From the intersecting graphs, it appears that it will take 55.8 months to repay the loan. In reality, it could take 55 months with the 55th payment being larger than \$250, or 56 months with the last payment being smaller than \$250. This last payment, sometimes called a *balloon payment*, is usually larger than the regular payments.

Page 21

1. The zeros are exactly $x = -2, 1, 4$, and the turning points are approximately $(-0.726, 10.392)$ and $(2.734, -10.392)$.

2. The only zero is $x = -0.823$, and there is no turning point.

3. The zeros are approximately $x = 0.38$ and $x = 2.62$. The turning point, here an absolute minimum value, is located at the point $(1.78, -15.827)$.

4. The only zero is $x = -1.32$ and the turning points are $(-0.58, 1.38)$ and $(0.58, 0.62)$.

5. This function has no real zeros, but the three turning points are $(-0.76, 8.62)$, $(0, 9)$, and $(0.76, 8.62)$.

6. The zeros are $x = -1$, $x = -2$, $x = 1$ and the turning points are $(-1.69, -0.397)$, $(-1, 0)$, and $(0.462, -2.83)$.

7. The zeros are $x = -0.7$, $x = -0.17$, $x = 1.09$, $x = 3.79$ and the turning points are $(-0.46, 0.89)$, $(0.548, -3.15)$, and $(2.90, 35.258)$.

8. This function has four zeros, at $x = -4.375$, $x = 0.44$, $x = 1.37$, $x = 4.555$. The turning points are $(-2.89, -156.70)$, $(0.9, 4.21)$, and $(3.48, -54.44)$.

9. The zeros are $x = -2.44$, $x = -1$, $x = 0$, $x = 2.44$, $x = 4$ and the turning points are $(-1.94, 24.23)$, $(-0.51, -6.47)$, $(1.43, 35.32)$ and $(3.41, -49.94)$.

Page 25

1. If the base is a circle with diameter x, the girth will be the circumference, which is πx, and the length L cannot exceed $108 - \pi x$. The formula for volume is $\pi \frac{x^2}{4} L$, or $\pi \frac{x^2}{4}(108 - \pi x)$. The maximum volume for this container is 14,851 in^3 and the box has a diameter of 22.9 inches.

2. The function for the total length of the three sections of cable is $f(x) = \sqrt{(x-10)^2 + 5^2} + \sqrt{x^2 + 10^2} + \sqrt{(x-20)^2 + 15^2}$. The minimum total length is approximately 37.13 units and occurs when $x = 9.51$.

Page 28

1. We need to solve the equation $0.04e^{0.065t} = 0.50$, or $0.04e^{0.065t} - 0.50 = 0$. This will occur when $x = 38.86$ or roughly near the end of 1996, if the model continues to hold. Using the same model it will take 49.52 years to reach \$1.00. This will be the year 2007.

2. We need to set $150 + 450\cos\left(\frac{\pi x}{6}\right) = 500$ and solve for x. The two values between 0 and 12 are 1.297 and 10.703. This means that from late November through early February the store sells over $500 of ski equipment each day.

Page 31

1. The cosine and the line $y = x$ intersect only once, at the point $(0.7391, 0.7391)$.

2. The graphs of $y = x$ and $y = \frac{1}{3}e^x$ intersect twice. The first point is at $(0.6191, 1.8573)$. This is an **attracting fixed point**, as all points around it are attracted to it. The other point is a **repelling fixed point**, as points are repelled from it. To find the other point you must use the inverse of $y = \frac{1}{3}e^x$, which is $y = \ln(3x)$. When you use the log function, the repelling point becomes an attracting point and Picard's method locates it at $(1.5121, 4.5363)$. We conclude that $x = 0.6191$ and $x = 1.5121$ are solutions.

3. Since both of these functions are even, the points of intersection will be symmetric with respect to the y-axis. To find the one in the first quadrant, use $y = x$ and $y = \sqrt{\cos x}$. The points of intersection are $(0.8241, 0.6791)$ and $(-0.8241, 0.6791)$. We conclude that $x = 0.8241$ and $x = -0.8241$ are solutions.

Page 33

1. The standard viewing window $-10 \le x \le 10$ and $-10 \le y \le 10$ is a good viewing window to show the local behavior. You can also graph the horizontal asymptote $y = 3$ on the same graph. If you zoom out by a factor of 3 ($-30 \le x \le 30$ and $-30 \le y \le 30$) most of the graph looks like the asymptote, but there is an abrupt deviation from this line near $x = 2$.

2. The standard viewing window $-10 \le x \le 10$ and $-10 \le y \le 10$ is a good viewing window to show the local behavior. You can also graph the oblique asymptote $y = x - 3$ along with the graph. If you zoom out by a factor of 3 ($-30 \le x \le 30$ and $-30 \le y \le 30$) most of the graph looks like the asymptote, but there is an abrupt deviation from this line near $x = 2$.

3. Regardless of the viewing window, the graph of this function is going to look like the line $y = x + 2$. The hole in the graph at the point $(3, 5)$ will be very difficult to see on the calculator.

4. If you graph this function using the viewing window $-5 \le x \le 5$ and $-5 \le y \le 15$, you will notice that the graph looks a lot like a parabola, except near $x = 2$. The line $x = 2$ is a vertical asymptote, but the rational function is asymptotic to the parabola $y = x^2 + x - 1$ as you move away from $x = 2$.

5. Since this graph is identical to the graph of $y = \frac{1}{x-4}$, except for a hole at the point $(0,0)$, a good window for viewing the local behavior might be $-2 \leq x \leq 10$ and $-10 \leq y \leq 10$. Zooming out by a factor of 3 reveals the global behavior. This function is very close to zero for most x-values, excepting near $x = 4$.

Page 35

1. If the airline only services one city, it just taxis from one end of the runway to the other. Two cities would give the airline 1 route; three cities 3 routes; four cities 6 routes; and so on. The points to fit the curve through are (1,0), (2,1), (3,3), and (4,6). The four cubic functions that equal zero at three of the x-values and equal the y-coordinate at the fourth x-coordinate are $y_1 = 1(x-1)(x-2)(x-3)$, $y_2 = 0(x-2)(x-3)(x-4)$, $y_3 = -\frac{3}{2}(x-1)(x-2)(x-4)$ and $y_4 = \frac{1}{2}(x-1)(x-3)(x-4)$.

   When these four functions are added togther, the sum is simply $f(x) = \frac{x(x-1)}{2}$.

Page 38

1. $\left(1 + \frac{0.06}{12}\right)^{12} = 1.0617$, so the effective rate is 6.17%.

2. Here $e^{0.08} = 1.0833$, so the effective rate is 8.33%.

3. For small values of n, the two functions are farther apart as x gets larger. For large values of n, the functions are still not equal, but they stay closer much longer. Because of the resolution on the graphing calculator, it is difficult to see this. Try letting $n = 1$ and graphing on the window $30 \leq x \leq 35$ and $5 \leq y \leq 7$. Now let $n = 12$ and notice the difference.

Page 40

1. There are any number of ways to solve for x if $50000(1 + .07)^x = 250000$: tracing and zooming; using a table of values; using a numerical method like Bisection; or solving algebraically. The algebraic solution is $\ln(5) \div \ln(1.07) = 23.79$

2. Again, this is simply $1700(1.10)^{18} = 9451.86$. Let's hope they also added some to it on a regular basis. See the section on annuities for a way to compute the amount in an account into which money is added on a regular basis.

Page 42

1. Either by using the formula, $f(x) = \frac{250(1.0075^x - 1)}{0.0075}$, or the recursive formula in the program, the amount would be $48,378.57.

2. The total in the account would be $42,111.06.

3. Start with $750,000 and take out $50,000. With this in the calculator as the last answer, press Ans, multiply by 1.08 and subtract 50000. Now press EXE. This is the first day of the second year. Press EXE 19 more times, and you now have $948,677.58 in the account. You could afford to pay yourself more each year.

4. If your parents put $600 in each year for 18 years, and the account is compounded only once each year, at the end of 18 years, there will be $36,811.36 in the account. This amount is $27,359.50 more than if your parents had only invested the $1700. If the 10% were compounded monthly and they invested $50 each month, the account would yield $39,480.02.

Page 44

1. The scatter plot of the data shows that it is fairly linear, so the least-squares regression line should be an appropriate model.

   a. The least-squares line has equation $y = -0.043x + 2.179$.

   b. The slope tells us that for every degree the incline is raised, the ball takes 0.043 fewer seconds to roll down the incline.

   c. At 24 degrees, the ball should take approximately $-0.043(24) + 2.179$, or about 1.15 seconds.

   d. Let $-0.043x + 2.179 = 1$ and solve. $x = 27.4$ degrees.

   e. Obviously, if the angle is zero, it cannot take 2.179 seconds to roll. In the range we were given, the model is fairly good.

Page 48

1. Possible models follow, where t represents the years since 1981, that is, in 1981, $t = 0$.

$$f(t) = 92.0e^{.037t}$$
$$f(t) = 958.1e^{.076t}$$
$$f(t) = 4,227e^{.088t}$$

The Consumer Price Index is growing at a rate of roughly 3.7% annually. The cost of attending a public college is going up by about 7.6% per year while the cost of attending a private college is growing at a rate of 8.8%, more than double the Consumer Price Index.

2. a. This relationship looks like a power function.
   b. Taking the logs of both coordinates produces a line.
   c. The slope of the line is roughly 0.81, and the intercept is very close to zero.
   d. A function which models this relationship is $f(x) = x^{0.81}$.

Page 55

1. The period is 12 (months) and the amplitude is $\frac{14.65-9.68}{2} = 2.485$. The vertical shift is $14.65 - 2.485 = 12.165$. The graph has also been shifted approximately 3 units to the right. If x represents the the number of the month, (1 = January 21st), the equation is $y = 2.485\sin\left(\frac{\pi}{6}(x-3)\right)+12.165$.
2. The equation is $y = 220\sin(120\pi x)$.
3. The wave quickly approaches a square wave, a wave with period 2π which equals 1 for $2k\pi < x < (2k+1)\pi$ and -1 for $(2k+1)\pi < x < (2k+2)\pi$, k and integer.

Page 63

1. Define the following matrices A and B.

$$A = B = \begin{bmatrix} 1.005 & 0 \\ -1 & 0 \end{bmatrix}$$

Multiply $A \times B$ and store the result in A. Repeat this process 4 more times. On the 5th multiplication, store the answer in both A and B. The 5th power is now stored in both A and B.

Now, multiply A and B and store the result in A. Repeat this process 2 more times. Store the final result in both A and B. The 15th power is now stored in both A and B.

Now multiply A and B and store the 60th power in both A and B. Repeat this process 3 more times, storing the result in both A and B each time.

Now redefine A to be

$$A = [500000 \quad 2500].$$

Multiply $A \times B$. By trial and error vary the second entry in matrix A until the first entry in the product is 0. The second entry you choose will be the approximate amount that can be withdrawn each month, that is, \$2,751.07.

2. Define the following matrices A and B.

$$A = B = \begin{bmatrix} 1.005 & 0 \\ -1.00166 & 1.00166 \end{bmatrix}$$

Follow the process outlined in problem 1, above, to find the 480th power of A and B. Redefine A to be

$$A = [500000 \quad 2000].$$

Again use trial and error until the first entry in the product is 0. You will be able to withdraw approximately \$2,087.62 first month and eventually withdraw \$4,642.99 the last month. Answers may vary slightly depending on rounding and how values are entered.

Index

NOTES

NOTES